CONTENTS

TABLES

Investigation of the Possible Increased Incidence of Cancer in West Cumbria

Report of the Independent Advisory Group

Chairman: Sir Douglas Black

London   Her Majesty's Stationery Office

ISBN 0 11 321006 X

FIGURES

CHAPTER 1

INTRODUCTION

1.1 Sir Douglas Black was asked by the Minister of Health if he would head an independent inquiry into the possible increased incidence of cancer in the area adjacent to the Sellafield site following the Yorkshire Television (YTV) programme—"Windscale—the Nuclear Laundry"—shown on ITV on 1 November 1983. He asked a group of six experts in relevant fields to assist him (listed in Appendix I). The Department of Health and Social Security (DHSS) provided the Secretariat for the Inquiry. Observers from the Welsh Office and from the Scottish Home and Health Department (SHHD) were also present at the meetings.

1.2 The *terms of reference* for the Inquiry were:—

To look into the recently published claims of an increased incidence of cancer in the vicinity of the Sellafield site:—

1. examine the evidence concerning the alleged cluster of cancer cases in the village of Seascale;
2. consider the need for further research;
3. and make recommendations.

1.3 The Group was asked to act as speedily as was consistent with a rigorous investigation of the situation.

1.4 The Group first met on 22 November 1983. We decided that, while the area of greatest importance in our investigation was that immediately adjacent to Sellafield, we needed to put our investigations in the context of the incidence of cancer in the rest of Cumbria, and in England and Wales. We therefore encouraged the early completion of analyses of cancer incidence and mortality studies in England and Wales in general and in Cumbria in particular.

1.5 At the same time questions were being asked in Scotland about possible adverse effects of the discharges from Sellafield on the health of the population in South West Scotland. As there seemed to be some evidence that there were certain coastal areas with a raised incidence of leukaemia, the SHHD commissioned their own investigations and some of their results have been incorporated into this report. We thank the SHHD for permission to do this.

1.6 Our task was threefold:—

a. establishing the incidence of cancer in the area adjacent to Sellafield, and comparing it with the incidence of cancer in other areas in the United Kingdom and in Cumbria;

b. considering the available data on radiation exposure in the area adjacent to Sellafield and the evidence relating radiation exposure to cancer, thus assessing the likelihood that any radiation exposure could have caused any increased incidence of cancer detected in the area;

c. assessing other possible significant factors.

1.7 We took oral evidence from a number of people and representatives of Government Departments and other interested organisations (listed in Appendix II). Many of these also submitted written reports or suggested additional material that we should consider. We wish to thank the National Radiological Protection Board (NRPB) for the three reports they prepared at our request and British Nuclear Fuels plc (BNFL) for answering many queries throughout the period of the Inquiry.

1.8 Many others besides those listed in Appendix II suggested possible lines of research, or submitted written evidence, including details of individual case histories. We would like to thank these people for their submissions which were all carefully considered. The limitations imposed by space and sometimes by confidentiality do not permit us to list all these sources, but some are referred to in the text.

1.9 The Advisory Group visited Cumbria in January 1984 when we saw the Sellafield site and spoke to local medical staff and to Seascale's general practitioners. Subsequently there were several visits to the area by individual members and by the Secretariat for consultation on particular questions raised as work progressed. We are most grateful to Dr J D Terrell, District Medical Officer of West Cumbria Health Authority, and his staff for their assistance which facilitated our analysis of the available scientific data.

1.10 The Sellafield site includes a reprocessing plant for spent nuclear fuel. For that reason the airborne and liquid discharges are different in composition and quantity from those from other nuclear establishments in the United Kingdom. These discharges result in collective dose commitments to the public considerably greater than those from any other nuclear establishment in the United Kingdom (Figure 1.1).

1.11 In November 1983 an incident at the Sellafield site resulted in the release to sea of a quantity of liquid waste containing some solvent and a large quantity of the radionuclide Ruthenium-106, which emits beta rays and gamma rays. The discharge resulted in the appearance on the beaches of objects sufficiently contaminated with Ruthenium-106 that the Radiochemical Inspectorate of the Department of the Environment gave advice, endorsed by NRPB, that the public should avoid unnecessary use of the beaches. This incident was the subject of inquiries by the Nuclear Installation Inspectorate and the Department of the Environment, and of reports from NRPB and the Ministry of Agriculture, Fisheries and Food (MAFF).

1.12 We took the view that the incident itself fell outside the terms of reference of our Inquiry but that any insights the incident and subsequent investigations provided into the previous radiation exposure of the local population were relevant.

1.13 This report includes the results of several as yet unpublished epidemiological studies. We are satisfied that the conclusions we draw from the work we have quoted are unlikely to be changed substantially by any subsequent re-analyses, and we thank these authors for allowing us to refer to their work prior to publication. Where we make suggestions in the report for further work on a study we are frequently referring to the authors' own suggestions for improving the power of their study, and do not imply any criticism of the quality of the authors' work.

Figure 1.1 Collective dose commitments from liquid and airborne discharges during 1978, man Sv

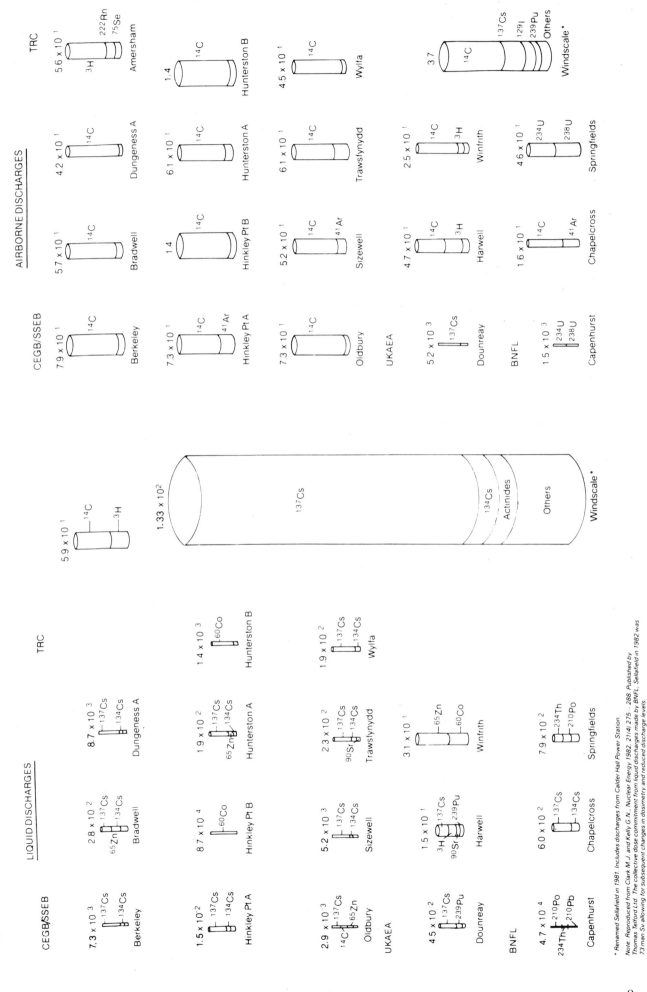

* Renamed Sellafield in 1981. Includes discharges from Calder Hall Power Station.

Note. Reproduced from Clark M J and Kelly G N, Nuclear Energy 1982, 21(4), 275 — 288. Published by Thomas Telford Ltd. The collective dose commitment from liquid discharges made by BNFL, Sellafield in 1982 was 73 man Sv allowing for subsequent changes in dosimetry and reduced discharge levels.

1.14 We have provided a Glossary of the technical terms that we could not avoid using, and underlined terms included in the Glossary the first time they appear in the text.

1.15 The Group met sixteen times in all and in addition there were several meetings of sub-groups to consider specific points in greater detail. The three reports which NRPB prepared following discussions with the Group give the scientific basis of much of the data in Chapter 4 for those who wish to assess the evidence on which we based our conclusions on radiation exposure in more detail.

1.16 Finally we would like to thank the DHSS for providing the Secretariat to assist us in our investigations. Our Secretaries have been helpful, courteous and efficient in supporting us through quite a complex investigation, and we are all most grateful to them. We should, of course, make it absolutely clear that the views expressed in this report are those of the Independent Advisory Group and not necessarily those of the Secretaries.

References

Clark M J and Kelly G N (1982) Radiation exposure of the UK population from routine discharges by civil nuclear installations. Nucl. Energy. *21*, 275–288.

Department of the Environment (1984) An incident leading to the contamination of the beaches near to the British Nuclear Fuels Ltd., Windscale and Calder Works, Sellafield, November 1983. A Report of Investigations into the circumstances by the Department of the Environment Radiochemical Inspectorate.

Health and Safety Executive (1984) The contamination of the beach incident at British Nuclear Fuels, Ltd., Sellafield, November 1983.

Ministry of Agriculture, Fisheries and Food (1983) Incident leading to contamination of beaches near British Nuclear Fuels, Ltd., Sellafield, November 1983. Monitoring and assessment of environmental consequences undertaken by Ministry of Agriculture, Fisheries and Food.

National Radiological Protection Board—M101 (1983) Analysis and radiological assessment of survey results and samples from the beaches around Sellafield. Webb, G A M and Fry, F A.

National Radiological Protection Board—M102 (1984) Assessment of survey results from the beaches around Sellafield. Webb, G A M and Fry, F A.

CHAPTER 2

EPIDEMIOLOGICAL
EVIDENCE AND RECOMMENDATIONS

BACKGROUND

2.1 Our initial concern was to establish whether or not there was an increased incidence or cluster of cancer, particularly in young people, in the area around Sellafield. The word cluster, which has a technical meaning related to a concentration of cases in space and time, will not be used in this Chapter because we are concerned with an extended time period.

2.2 Mr Cutler, the producer of the YTV film, told us that his original intention had been to look at the effects of occupational exposure to radiation in the nuclear power industry, and that initially he had approached BNFL at Sellafield with this in mind. BNFL had already published preliminary epidemiological studies on their workers (Clough 1983) and they agreed to co-operate. However, the attention of the YTV team was drawn to a number of children with leukaemia in Seascale. This led them to change the direction of their investigation, and to concentrate on the general population living near Sellafield.

2.3 The YTV study was carried out in an epidemiologically unconventional manner, cases of childhood cancer being identified by talking to local inhabitants and to the parents of affected children. Local registers were searched for deaths of children and death certificates obtained to establish the cause of death.

2.4 By proceeding in this way the YTV team collected information for the years 1956–83 on 7 young people with leukaemia who were under 22 years old at diagnosis, and living in Seascale. Using Census data they estimated that there was approximately a 10-fold higher incidence of leukaemia among children under 10 years old in Seascale when compared to the national incidence figures; this statement is based on 5 cases (Cutler 1983a).

2.5 The YTV team identified 25 young people under 22 years old with cancer in Millom Rural District dying or diagnosed between 1954 and 1983, including the 7 children with leukaemia in Seascale. These included 6 other young people with leukaemia, 2 children with lymphoma in Seascale, 3 young men with testicular teratoma in Millom Town, 3 children with brain tumours (one from Seascale), 3 children with sarcomas (one from Seascale) and one child with a kidney tumour (Urquhart 1983).

2.6 The YTV team claimed that the above findings demonstrated "a significant high excess of cancer and particularly leukaemia in children under 18 years old in the 5 coastal parishes south of Windscale in the last 25 years, and in the absence of any other readily apparent cause, the *possibility* of a link with environmental radioactivity from Windscale's discharges must be seriously investigated" (Cutler 1983b).

2.7 In a later television programme in April 1984 the YTV team claimed that there was an excess of cancer deaths among persons aged from 15–24 years in Maryport, a town to the north of Sellafield. They also referred to a further child in Seascale recently diagnosed as having cancer.

2.8 YTV had perforce to use unconventional and unsystematic methods to ascertain their cases. One of our tasks was to check the validity of their results. This included preparing, from official records where possible, a list of young people resident in the area who, since 1950 have died from cancer or have been diagnosed as suffering from cancer.

2.9 An exaggeration of the problem might have arisen in the way that the above data were used because the age group reported was defined by the ages of the discovered cases (paragraph 2.4). This is exemplified also in the statement in paragraph 2.6 with the choice of the age of 18 years as the upper limit. A statistically sounder method is first to define the age range of interest (0–14 years of age is most commonly used for childhood cancer) and then to ascertain the number of cases which fall within this defined range.

2.10 Selection of specific geographical areas for study on the basis of cases of cancer discovered in them may also lead to an artificial result. This can be seen by considering what would happen if there were 4 cases of leukaemia diagnosed in a particular town. The 4 (or fewer) streets where the 4 cases lived would each have a 'high' incidence of leukaemia, while all the other streets would have a zero incidence. This result would be a true description of the incidence of leukaemia in the different streets of the town. However it might reflect, not an aetiological influence peculiar to those streets, but merely the fact that 4 cases of leukaemia cannot occur in more than 4 streets. Similarly, if parishes are selected for study because cases of cancer are known to have occurred there, it is not surprising if the incidence of cancer in those parishes is found to be unusually high. The same comments apply to similar selection of certain calendar years, disease categories and age ranges for study.

DETAILS OF THE INDEX CASES

2.11 Tables 2.1–2.4 include those cases of leukaemia and other forms of cancer known to us by 1st June 1984 in the under 25 year old population of Millom Rural District based on information from YTV, death certificate data and the preliminary findings from an intensive review of hospital records being carried out for us by the West Cumbria Health Authorities. All of the studies considered below have included some of these index cases, grouping them variously according to time, age, sex, area and disease classification. It should be emphasised that the cases shown in the Tables may well be an incomplete list.

Table 2.1   Cases of leukaemia resident in Seascale since 1955 and aged under 25 years at diagnosis‡

Case No	Year of Birth	Place of Birth*	Year of Diagnosis	Year of Death	Place of Death**	Sex	Diagnosis‡
Case 1	1947	Outside Millom Rural District	1955	1956	Seascale	F	Acute lymphatic leukaemia
Case 2	1957	Outside Millom Rural District	1968	Alive	—	M	Acute lymphocytic leukaemia
Case 3	1957	Seascale	1960	1960	Seascale	M	Acute myeloid leukaemia
Case 4	1958	Seascale	1978	1979	Seascale	M	Chronic myeloid leukaemia
Case 5	1964	Seascale	1968	1970	Seascale	M	Chronic lymphocytic leukaemia
Case 6	1968	Seascale	1971	1971	Seascale	F	Acute lymphoblastic leukaemia
Case 7	1974	Seascale	1979	Alive	—	F	Acute lymphoblastic leukaemia

*Residential address of mother at time of birth
**Residential address at time of death
‡As recorded by certifying doctor

Table 2.2 Cases of leukaemia in Millom Rural District since 1955 and aged under 25 years at diagnosis‡ excluding cases in Seascale

Case No	Year of Birth	Place of Birth*	Year of Diagnosis	Year of Death	Place of Death**	Sex	Diagnosis‡
Case 8	1946	Other Millom Rural District°	1963	1964	Other Millom Rural District°	F	Erythroleukaemia
Case 9	1952	Other Millom Rural District°	1971	1971	Other Millom Rural District°	M	Acute myeloid leukaemia
Case 10	1953	Outside Millom Rural District		1973	Other Millom Rural District°	F	Acute lymphoblastic leukaemia
Case 11	1957	Other Millom Rural District°	1973	1974	Other Millom Rural District°	F	Acute myeloblastic leukaemia
Case 12	1957	Other Millom Rural District°	1957	1968	Other Millom Rural District°	M	Acute myelomonoblastic leukaemia
Case 13	?1963		?1984		Other Millom Rural District°		Leukaemia
Case 28	1939	Other Millom Rural District°	1958			F	Acute myeloid leukaemia

*Residential address of mother at time of birth
**Residential address at time of death
‡As recorded by certifying doctor
°Other Millom Rural District means Millom Rural District except Seascale

Table 2.3   Cases of lymphoma resident in Millom Rural District under 25 years at Diagnosis‡

Case No	Year of Birth	Place of Birth*	Year of Diagnosis	Year of Death	Place of Death**	Sex	Diagnosis‡
Case 14	1952	Seascale	1955	1955	Outside Millom Rural District	F	Lympho-sarcoma
Case 15	1961	Other Millom Rural District°	1984	Alive	—	F	Histio-cytosis X
Case 16	1974	Outside Millom Rural District	1983	Alive	—	M	?Non Hodgkin's Lymphoma
Case 17	1982	Seascale	1983	Alive	—	F	Non Hodgkin's Lymphoma
Case 29	1956	Other Millom Rural District°	1975	Alive	—	M	Lymphocytic Leukaemia
Case 30	1961	Other Millom Rural District°	1980	Alive	—	M	Hodgkin's Disease
Case 31	1961	Other Millom Rural District°	1982	Alive	—	F	Hodgkin's Disease
Case 32		Other Millom Rural District°		1969		M	Hodgkin's Disease

*Residential address of mother at time of birth
**Residential address at time of death
‡As recorded by certifying doctor
°Other Millom Rural District means Millom Rural District except Seascale

Table 2.4   Cases of solid tumours resident in Millom Rural District under 25 years at diagnosis‡

Case No	Year of Birth	Place of Birth*	Year of Diagnosis	Year of Death	Place of Death**	Sex	Diagnosis‡
Case 18	1955			1973	Millom Town	M	Teratoma of Testes
Case 19	1960			1976	Millom Town	M	Teratoma of Testes
Case 20	1964		1981	Alive	Millom Town	M	Teratoma of Testes
Case 21	1969	Outside Millom Rural District	1981	Alive		F	Suprasellar Teratoma
Case 22	1948	Seascale		1954	Seascale	M	Neuroblastoma of Adrenal
Case 23	1948	Other Millom Rural District°	June 1965	Alive	—	M	Cerebellar Astrocytoma
Case 24	1969	Outside Millom Rural District		1973	Millom Rural District	F	Neuroblastoma of kidney
Case 25	1955	Seascale		1964	Other Millom Rural District°	F	Sarcoma
Case 26	1969	Seascale		1975	Seascale	F	Retroperitoneal sarcoma
Case 27	1966	Outside Millom Rural District	1978	1979	Other Millom Rural District°	M	Ewing's Sarcoma of rib

*Residential address of mother at time of birth
**Residential address at time of death
‡As recorded by the certifying doctor
°Other Millom Rural District means Millom Rural District outside Seascale

2.12 Seascale is not a typical West Cumbrian village. We were told that the Ministry of Supply and the United Kingdom Atomic Energy Authority (UKAEA) built much of the accommodation in the village to house its staff before and at the time that the Windscale <u>Piles</u> were under construction in 1952. We believe that BNFL continues to own a significant proportion of the houses. These are rented mainly to young graduates, who are a mobile population, possibly more likely to be working with radioactive material than the average BNFL employee.

2.13 We were also told that the population of Seascale was more mobile than that of many adjacent villages. This could affect the estimated incidence of cancer in various ways. For instance, the annual size of the population is not known accurately as Censuses are only undertaken every 10 years. This results in uncertainty about the numbers to be used in each age group to calculate rates or expected numbers of cases. Also, when considering the effect of a local environmental carcinogen on the incidence of malignant disease in such an area, the latent period between exposure and the development of malignancy can result in under-ascertainment due to emigration of cases. Such population movement is of particular importance when considering the incidence of cancers with long latent intervals between exposure and diagnosis, such as were found for solid tumours in those exposed following the dropping of atom bombs at Hiroshima and Nagasaki.

2.14 Figure 2.1 shows that the annual number of births in Seascale was highest from 1950–1965, at around 50 births per year. It fell subsequently to around 15 births per year in the early 1970's. More recently there has been a slight increase to around 20 births per year (Stevenson and Walker, 1984).

2.15 Figure 2.2 shows that of the 28 cases of childhood cancer considered, 4 were born in 1957 and 1 in 1958. However, only Case 3 was *in utero* in the area at the time of the Windscale fire in 1957; Case 4 was conceived around the time of the fire; and the birth of Case 2 was registered in Oxford. The other two cases (Numbers 11 and 12) were 5 months and 7 months old at the time of the fire. (Details of cases 29–32 were received too late to be included in this Table.)

Figure 2.1 Number of births/year in Seascale*

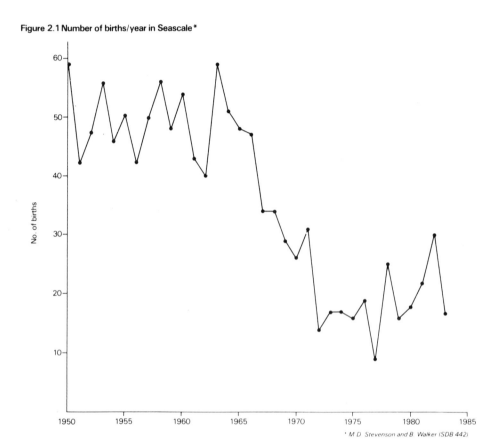

* M.D. Stevenson and B. Walker (SDB 442)

Figure 2.2a Year of diagnosis of cases in Tables 2.1 – 2.4

Key

° Born outside Cumbria	Cases 1 – 7 = Seascale Leukaemia
• Year of Death (year of diagnosis not available)	Cases 8 – 13 and 28 = Rest of Millom RD Leukaemia
· Year unconfirmed	Cases 14 – 17 = Millom RD lymphoma
	Cases 18 – 27 = Millom RD solid tumour

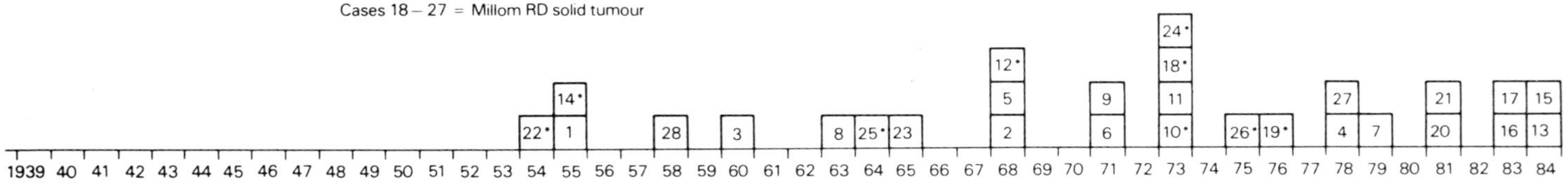

Figure 2.2b Year of birth of cases in Tables 2.1 – 2.4

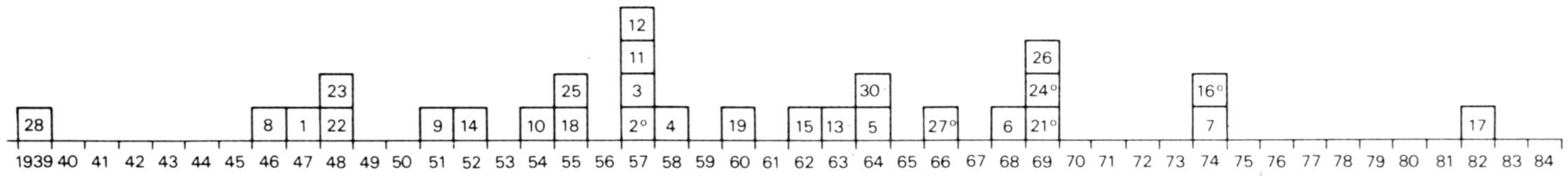

2.16 *In utero* exposure to radiation via medical X-rays or nuclear medicine investigations was considered as a potential contributary cause. Of the 4 Seascale leukaemia cases for which the ante-natal notes have so far been traced, one had been exposed to diagnostic radiography during the last week of pregnancy (Case 6). One of the lymphomas (Case 14) had 4 X-ray exposures 3 weeks before birth. No details of X-ray exposure of the other 3 lymphomas have been obtained yet.

2.17 All of the fathers of the seven Seascale leukaemia cases, and three of the fathers of the five Seascale cases of other cancers worked at BNFL. These are not unexpected proportions given the predominance of BNFL employees resident in Seascale.

THE INCIDENCE OF CANCER IN CUMBRIA

2.18 Concern about patterns of cancer incidence and possible underlying causes is not a new phenomenon. Cumberland has been an area of interest to epidemiologists for many years, and a study of lung cancer in haematite miners in West Cumberland was reported as early as 1956 (Faulds and Stewart, 1956; Boyd et al, 1970). Studies on the incidence of cancer in Cumbria has been undertaken, and studies on cancer incidence around nuclear installations in the UK were in progress, before the YTV programme raised public interest. Table 2.5 gives summary details of some of the relevant studies which we have been able to examine.

Table 2.5 Summary of studies on the incidence of cancer in Cumbria

Study	Incidence Study	Death Rate Study	Period	Age Range in years	Diseases	Area
Tiplady	+	+	1951–77	All ages	All diseases	W Cumbria
Alderson, Ashwood and	+	–	1961–80	0–14 15–74	All cancers Selected Cancers	Copeland District
Cook-Mozafarri	–	+	1959–80	0–14 15–74	All Leukaemias	
P Cook-Mozafarri	–	+	1969–78	0–24 25–44 45–64 65+	Leukaemia Radiation associated cancer Other cancer	Copeland District
Craft and Birch	+	–	1968–82	0–14	Cancer and acute lympho-blastic Leukaemia	Cumbria South Lakeland and Barrow
Urquhart Palmer and Cutler	–	+	1963–82	0–24	All Cancers Leukaemia	Seascale and coastal villages, Millom RD, Copeland,
	+	–	1968–83	0–14	All Cancers	
	–	+	1963–72 1973–82	15–24	All Cancers	Copeland Millom RD Allerdale Maryport
Palmer	–	+	1963–82	0–24	Leukaemia All Cancers	Five coastal parishes
Gardner and Winter	–	+	1968–78	All ages	All Causes All Cancers Leukaemia	Cumbria
	–	+	1959–67 1968–78	All ages 0–24	All Causes All Cancers Leukaemia	Millom RD Ennerdale RD Local Authority areas in Cumbria
Craft and Openshaw	+	–	1968–82	0–14	All Cancers All Lymphoid malignancies	Northern Children's Cancer Registry area
Gardner and Winter	–	+	1968–78	0–24	Leukaemia	152 Rural Districts

Key
+ Included in study
– Not included in study

2.19 The Cumbria Area Health Authority published a report 'Leukaemia and other cancers in Cumbria' May, 1981 (Tiplady, 1981), which was later updated (Tiplady, 1983). Data on mortality from and registrations of leukaemia and other cancers for the period 1951–1980 were presented for Cumbria as a whole, and for East, West and South-West Cumbria Districts.

2.20 Leukaemia mortality in Cumbria 1951–1978 was lower than national rates when all ages are considered together. Overall death rates from leukaemia have doubled, both in Cumbria and in England and Wales, over this time period. However, in England and Wales these increases were restricted to persons over 75 years of age, whereas at some younger ages there have been decreases.

2.21 In West Cumbria, the age-standardised incidence of malignant disease among both men and women during 1969–77 was significantly lower than in England and Wales overall (Tables 2.6 and 2.7), and had not altered to a statistically significant extent when the incidence in 1974–1977 was compared with that in 1969–1973. When leukaemia is considered, again the

Table 2.6 Registrations of malignant neoplasms of lymphatic and haemopoietic tissue
West Cumbria (Males)

ICD Number		1969–1973			1974–1977			Significance of trend 1969/1973 to 1974/1977
		Number of Cases	Crude registration rates per million per year	Standardised registration ratios (SRR)	Number of Cases	Crude registration rates per million per year	Standardised registration ratios (SRR)	
200	Lymphosarcoma, and reticulm cell sarcoma	12	35·8	98·4	3	11·4	29·5*	**
201	Hodgkin's Disease	11	32·8	100·5	10	30·4	107·5	
203	Multiple Myeloma	13	38·8	148·0	9	30·4	99·6	
204	Lymphatic Leukaemia	4	11·9	34·7	15	53·3	145·4	**
205	Myeloid Leukaemia	8	23·9	80·2	9	34·2	100·1	
206	Monocytic Leukaemia	—	—	—	—	—	—	
207	Other and Unspecified Leukaemia	3	9·0	111·6	3	11·4	145·7	
204–207	All Leukaemias	15	44·8	60·0*	27	98·9	117·6	**
140–209	All Malignancies	1,003	2,293·0	90·2*	922	3,306·7	93·5*	

Table 2.7 Registrations of malignant neoplasms of lymphatic and haemopoietic tissue
West Cumbria (Females)

ICD Number		1969–1973			1974–1977			Significance of trend 1969/1973 to 1974/1977
		Number of Cases	Crude registration rates per million per year	Standardised registration ratios (SRR)	Number of Cases	Crude registration rates per million per year	Standardised registration ratios (SRR)	
200	Lymphosarcoma, and reticulm cell sarcoma	8	26·1	177·4	7	25·1	81·2	
201	Hodgkin's Disease	8	23·2	114·0	3	7·2	49·1	
203	Multiple Myeloma	11	31·9	131·7	11	35·8	126·7	
204	Lymphatic Leukaemia	11	31·9	151·9	7	25·1	154·8	
205	Myeloid Leukaemia	10	29·0	113·3	5	17·9	52·9	
206	Monocytic Leukaemia	—	—	—	—	—	—	
207	Other and Unspecified Leukaemia	3	8·7	111·6	3	14·3	145·7	
204–207	All Leukaemias	24	69·6	129·0	15	57·3	84·7	
140–209	All Malignancies	897	2,605·4	89·3*	872	2,951·3	91·0*	

(Tiplady, 1981, 1983)

*Indicates SRR significantly differs from 100 at p <0·025
**Indicates difference between SRR's 1969/73 and 1974/77, significant at p <0·025

incidence was not significantly higher than expected in either sex. There were decreases in the registration rates for lymphosarcoma and reticulm cell sarcoma, but these are likely to be related to changes in diagnostic classification, which are known to have taken place nationally.

2.22 This evidence, while reassuring in that it demonstrates a generally low incidence of malignancy in West Cumbria considers all ages together and relatively large geographical areas. It does not exclude the possibility of a localised excess of cancer in young people living near Sellafield.

2.23 The Office of Population Censuses and Surveys (OPCS) study (Alderson et al 1984) used death certificate and cancer registry data to examine the incidence of cancer in Copeland District (Millom Rural District, Ennerdale Rural District and Whitehaven Municipal Borough) (Fig 2.3).

Figure 2.3 The Post-1974 County of Cumbria

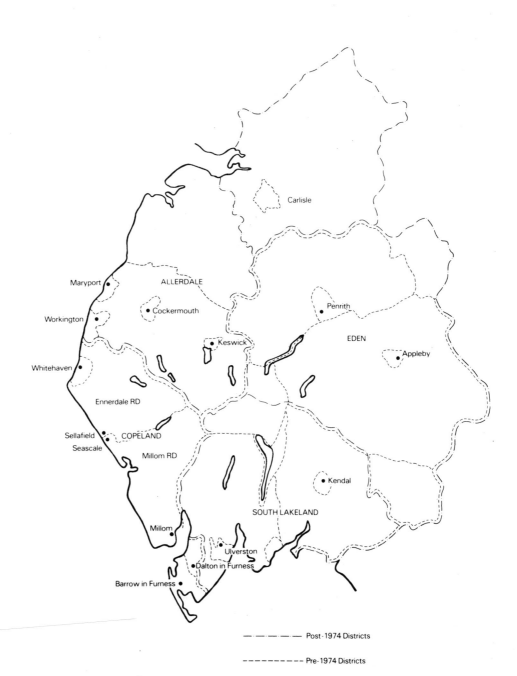

————— Post-1974 Districts

--------- Pre-1974 Districts

The population was separated into a 0–14 year age group and a 15–74 year age group. As mentioned in paragraph 2.9, 0–14 years is the commonly accepted age-span for studying childhood tumours. Death certificate data for the period 1959–80 and incidence data for 1961–80 were used. A control location was selected which 'matched' the Sellafield location (Copeland District) consisting of Penrith Rural District, North Westmorland Rural District and Kendal Municipal Borough.

2.24 Census data for 1961, 1971 and 1981 were used for population estimates. Expected numbers were calculated using incidence and mortality rates by 5-year age-groups, for males and females separately, in the most appropriate 'standard' population. This was thought to be the Northern Region less the Tyne and Wear conurbation.

2.25 The results showed increased rates for leukaemia (all types aggregated) and lymphoid leukaemia in 0–14 year old males in Copeland District (Table 2.8) but not in females. When the 22 year period of the study was subdivided into 3 shorter periods (1959–65, 1966–75, 1976–80) there was no evidence for an increase in the Standardised Mortality Ratio (SMR) or the Standardised Registration Ratio (SRR) across the 3 periods when compared to the changes in the control location for either all cancers, all leukaemia or lymphoid leukaemia (Table 2.9). The population figures used in the OPCS study were approximate, but the study was considered adequate by the authors to identify a twofold increase in cancer rates.

Table 2.8   Cancer deaths and registrations in Copeland District

Site	Sex	1959–80 Cancer Deaths 0–14 years			1961–80 Cancer Registrations 0–14 years		
		Observed	Expected	SMR	Observed	Expected	SRR
All Malignant Sites	M	16	15·2	105·3	29	19·81	146·4
	F	9	10·26	87·7	12	14·45	83·0
Testis	M	0	0·09	0·0	1	0·4	250·0
All leukaemias (21–25)	M	10	6·67	149·9	14	5·99	233·7**
	F	3	4·43	67·7	5	4·5	111·1
Lymphoid Leukaemia	M	7	5·46	128·2	11	4·76	231·1*
	F	3	3·62	82·9	4	3·66	109·3
Myeloid Leukaemia	M	3	0·85	352·9	2	0·76	263·2
	F	0	0·70	0·0	0	0·61	0·0

Other sites studied and giving SMR/SRR not statistically significant were:— liver, bone, thyroid, all lymphoid, multiple myeloma, monocytic leukaemia, other leukaemia, leukaemia unspecified, lung, Hodgkin's , lymphosarcoma/lymphoid, benign brain/nervous, unspecified brain/nervous

(Alderson et al, 1984)

*p <0·05
**p <0·01

Table 2.9   Comparison of SMR's and SRR's for Copeland and Control location for three time periods, by sex, site of malignancy, and age

Age Years	Site	Sex	Location	SMRs				SRRs			
				1959–65	1966–75	1976–80	No.	1961–65	1966–75	1976–80	No.
0–14	All Malignancies	M	Copeland	100	100	136	16	105	144	206	29
			Control	65	120	—	7	102	119	173	15
		F	Copeland	84	124	—	9	58	102	63	12
			Control	—	33	170	3	56	122	195	11
	All Leukaemia	M	Copeland	141	199	—	10	224	262	172	14
			Control	—	56	—	1	—	54	—	1
		F	Copeland	119	47	—	3	82	87	204	5
			Control	—	—	246	1	157	68	318	4
	Lymphoid Leukaemia	M	Copeland	141	146	—	7	224	236	231	11
			Control	—	—	—	0	—	—	—	0
		F	Copeland	119	61	—	3	82	114	145	4
			Control	—	—	514	1	157	88	456	4
15–74	All Malignancies	M	Copeland	99	97	91	1,353	96	84	89	1,582
			Control	72	81	82	860	57	69	85	983
		F	Copeland	102	102	108	1,074	97	87	96	1,465
			Control	91	94	89	733	73	77	96	983
	All Leukaemia	M	Copeland								
			Control	104	109	164	29	18	89	119	21
		F	Copeland	89	173	131	34	84	148	118	31
			Control	154	111	129	24	138	77	153	21
	Lymphoid Leukaemia	M	Copeland	109	70	38	16	78	91	96	18
			Control	104	109	206	17	18	88	95	10
		F	Copeland	89	248	55	19	84	255	46	19
			Control	154	149	71	15	138	129	116	13

(Alderson et al, 1984)

2.26 Dr P Cook-Mozaffari, as well as collaborating with the Office of Population Censuses and Surveys in the above investigation, is continuing a study of cancer rates around nuclear establishments initiated by Dr J A Baron. Preliminary results have shown raised leukaemia mortality in Copeland among persons under the age of 25 years during 1969–78 compared to England and Wales and to other rural Cumbrian districts.

2.27 A study based on data from the Manchester Children's Tumour Registry (set up in 1954) and the Northern Children's Cancer Registry (set up in 1968) reported cancer incidence rates and acute lymphoblastic leukaemia incidence rates in children under 15 years of age on an area basis (Craft and Birch, 1983). The incidence rates in Copeland District, which includes Sellafield (Figure 2.3) were among the highest of six areas examined in three time periods (1968–72, 1973–77 and 1978–82) (Table 2.10). However, there was no suggestion of any distinctive consistent pattern.

Table 2.10 Incidence per 100,000 person-years of all malignant disease and of acute lymphoblastic leukaemia in children under 15, resident in Cumbria 1968–82

Area	1968–72	1973–77	1978–82
All Malignant Disease			
Carlisle	6·7(8)	6·1(7)	9·6(10)
Allerdale	6·3(7)	9·4(10)	11·6(11)
Eden	17·6(9)	6·3(3)	11·4(5)
Copeland*	15·8(15)	10·6(9)	10·5(8)
S. Lakeland	14·7(15)	10·2(10)	8·8(8)
Barrow	9·8(9)	6·9(6)	13·0(10)
Acute Lymphoblastic Leukaemia			
Carlisle	1·6(2)	1·8(2)	1·9(2)
Allerdale	0·9(1)	3·8(2)	1·0(1)
Eden	0	0	0
Copeland*	6·3(6)	3·5(3)	2·6(2)
S. Lakeland	1·0(1)	5·1(5)	6·6(6)
Barrow	3·3(3)	1·2(1)	2·6(2)

*The Sellafield Site and Seascale village are in Copeland district. Figures in brackets are number of cases on which calculations are based.

(Craft and Birch, 1983)

2.28 All of the studies discussed in paragraphs 2.19–2.27 are open to the criticism that the geographical spread of the study was large and might conceal a local raised incidence of childhood leukaemia near Sellafield.

2.29 Cancer incidence and mortality in young people in smaller areas of Cumbria were examined by Urquhart, Palmer and Cutler (1984) using data obtained from OPCS. They found that 7 deaths from all cancers and 4 deaths from leukaemia had occurred in persons under 25 years of age in Seascale and four selected nearby coastal villages between 1963–82. These are statistically significant ($p < 0.02$ in each instance) excesses over the numbers expected on the basis of death rates for England and Wales (Table 2.11). In

Table 2.11 Deaths per 100,000 person-years 1963–82 (and numbers of deaths) for England and Wales and for selected parts of Cumbria

Age	England and Wales	Copeland	Millom RD*+	Seascale and Coastal Villages
All Malignancies				
0–14	6·7	6·2(22)	7·7(6)	19·7(4)
15–24	7·9	12·3(27)	20·9(9)	27·5(3)
0–24	7·2	8·5(49)	12·4(15)	22·4(7)
All Leukaemias				
0–14	2·8	2·8(10)	3·8(3)	9·7(2)
15–24	2·1	3·2(7)	11·6(5)	18·3(2)
0–24	2·5	3·0(17)	6·6(8)	12·7(4)

*The population of Millom Rural District is about 20% of that of Copeland. The coastal villages and Seascale are the five coastal parishes in Millom Rural District nearest Windscale to the South and consist of Seascale itself, Drigg and Carleton, Bootle, Waberthwaite, and Muncaster. The population is about 5% of that of Copeland.
+There were 50 non-cancer deaths in Millom Rural District in the under 15 age group and 20 in the 15–24 age group; the non-cancer death rates are similar to those for England and Wales.

(Urquhart et al 1984)

the same age group in Millom Rural District, which includes Seascale (Figure 2.3), 8 deaths occurred from leukaemia in the same period ($p < 0.01$). This paper also drew attention to an increase in the number of deaths from all cancers among the 15–24 years of age group in Maryport in 1973–82 as compared with 1963–72 (Table 2.12). However, no increase under the age of

Table 2.12 Deaths per 100,000 person-years from malignancy in 15–24 year old group (and numbers of deaths)

Years	E & W	Copeland	Millom RD*	Allerdale*	Maryport+
1963–72	8·4	12(11)	10(2)	—	0(0)
1973–82	7·4	14(16)	32(7)	6(7)	29(5)

*1974–81 only
+ Maryport is a small part of Allerdale.

(Urquhart et al, 1984)

15 years was found. Maryport harbour is one of several places along the coast where silt (containing traces of radioactive material discharged from Sellafield) is preferentially deposited, and the paper suggested a possible connection between these two phenomena. However, interpretation of this increase, as with others in the papers we have looked at, is made difficult by the many rates examined—the more rates that are examined, the more high ones will be found by chance alone. When small numbers of cases are involved these high rates can occur purely by chance, and have no particular local interpretation.

2.30 At our request Dr M K Palmer extended this work to an examination of deaths from cancer in the under 25 year old population of the 5 coastal parishes immediately south of Sellafield (Bootle, Drigg and Carleton, Seascale, Muncaster and Waberthwaite) compared with the rest of Millom Rural District for the years 1963–80 (Tables 2.13 and 2.14). He found a greater

Table 2.13 Comparison of Observed and Expected Leukaemia Deaths in Millom RD during 1963–80

Age Group	5 Coastal Parishes			Rest of Millom RD		
	O	E	O/E	O	E	O/E
0–4	1	0·17	5·9	0	0·37	0
5–14	1	0·34	3·0	1	0·71	1·4
15–24	2	0·18	11·0	3	0·54	5·6
Total	4	0·69	5·8	4	1·62	2·5
Statistical Significance		p=0·005			p=0·08	

(Palmer, 1984)

O=Observed deaths
E=Expected deaths

Table 2.14 Comparison of Observed and Expected Deaths from Cancers other than Leukaemia in Millom RD during 1963–80

Age Group	5 Coastal Parishes			Rest of Millom RD		
	O	E	O/E	O	E	O/E
0–4	1	0·30	3·3	0	0·68	0
5–14	1	0·50	2·0	0	1·05	0
15–24	2	0·63	3·2	1	1·87	0·5
Total	4	1·43	2·8	1	3·60	0·3
Statistical Significance		p=0·065			—	

(Palmer, 1984)

O=Observed deaths
E=Expected deaths

than five-fold excess (statistically significant) of deaths from leukaemia in the under 25 year old population of these five coastal parishes (4 observed cases, 0·69 expected; p=0·005), and a 2·5-fold excess (not quite statistically significant) of deaths from leukaemia in the under 25 year old population of the rest of Millom Rural District (4 observed, 1·62 expected; p=0·08). Mortality from cancers other than leukaemia in young people under 25 years of age was also raised in the five coastal parishes (4 observed, 1·43 expected), which approaches the conventional level of statistical significance; in the remainder of Millom Rural District only one death from these cancers occurred compared to 3·60 expected. It must be noted that there are coastal parishes to the north of Sellafield, and also others further to the south than the five collectively grouped.

2.31 Gardner and Winter (1984a) examined data obtained for the Atlas of Cancer Mortality for England and Wales (Gardner et al 1983) which covered the years 1968–78. For Cumberland during this period at all ages there were deficits of 6% for men and 2% for women in the number of cancer deaths observed when compared with the numbers expected at national death rates, and slightly fewer leukaemias than expected (Table 2.15). Among specific

Table 2.15 Mortality by cause of death and sex in Cumberland during 1968–78

Cause	Men			Women		
	O	E	SMR	O	E	SMR
All	20,904	19,801	106*	19,755	18,570	106*
Non-cancer	16,811	15,464	109*	16,213	14,961	108*
Cancer	4,093	4,338	94*	3,542	3,608	98
Leukaemia	104	113·2	92	96	93·5	103

Key

O=Observed; E=Expected number of deaths at age, sex and cause specific rates in England and Wales 1968–78;

SMR= 100 ×(O/E)=Standardised Mortality Ratio. ICD 8 numbers are 140–209 for cancer and 204–207 for leukaemia.

*Significantly different from 100 at p<0·01.

(Gardner and Winter, 1984a)

types of cancer there were significant excesses (10–15%) for stomach, large intestine and pancreas. When Millom Rural District (containing Seascale) and Ennerdale Rural District (containing the Sellafield site, figure 2.3) were considered separately, the death rates at all ages were similar to those for Cumberland as a whole except for a raised leukaemia rate in Millom Rural District, which was not statistically significant (Table 2.16). If the under 25 year old group only is considered, there were apparent raised cancer death-rates in both areas during 1968–78 but not during the earlier years 1959–67. In Millom Rural District the excess was largely accounted for by leukaemia, for which there was a four-fold excess in the 1968–78 period, but this was not the case in Ennerdale Rural District. Looking at leukaemia deaths in young people under 25 years of age in Cumberland during 1959–67, there were statistically significant excesses in Carlisle County Borough and Wigton Rural District, while in the later period 1968–78 only Millom Rural District had a statistically significant excess.

Table 2.16 Mortality by cause of death and age in Ennerdale and Millom Rural Districts

Cause	Time period	Ennerdale RD			Millom RD		
		O	E	SMR	O	E	SMR
All ages							
All causes	1959–67	—	—	—	—	—	—
	1968–78	3,897	3,684	106*	1,785	1,737	103
Cancer	1959–67	564	548·5	103	234	266·9	88+
	1968–78	726	765·6	95	330	359·7	92
Leukaemia	1959–67	15	15·6	96	6	7·6	79
	1968–78	16	20·6	78	13	9·5	137
Age 0–24 yr							
All causes	1959–67	—	—	—	—	—	—
	1968–78	167	145·8	115	63	60·5	104
Cancer	1959–67	7	9·1	77	3	4·5	67
	1968–78	14	9·3	150	10	4·0	253+
Leukaemia	1959–67	3	3·3	91	1	1·6	63
	1968–78	4	3·3	121	6	1·4	435*

All causes figures not calculated for 1959–67; ICD 7 (1959–67) and ICD 8 (1968–78) numbers are, respectively, 140–207 and 140–209 for cancer and 204 and 204–207 for leukaemia.

Significantly different from 100 at *$p<0.01$, +$p<0.05$.

(Gardner and Winter, 1984a)

2.32 Assessment of the above data is complicated by the fact that these studies did not use the same periods of time, age groups and/or geographical areas. The selection depended mainly on the sources of data (Table 2.5). Where large areas are looked at, possible local excesses disappear. Using smaller areas excesses of childhood cancers are found in certain areas, but this approach increases the possibility that statistically significant excesses are found by chance as more areas are examined. The data collected by the YTV team spans the longest period.

2.33 The above results can be summarised as suggesting an approximately four-fold higher rate of leukaemia mortality in the under 25 year old population in Millom Rural District during 1968–78—or twofold during 1959–78 (Gardner and Winter, 1984)—and an approximately 10-fold higher rate of leukaemia incidence in the under 10 year old population of Seascale (paragraph 2.4; Urquhart et al 1984). No unusual cancer rates are found among the over 25 year old population of Millom Rural District or in Ennerdale Rural District.

CANCER INCIDENCE DATA FOR SMALL AREAS IN THE UNITED KINGDOM

2.34 The above results suggested that Seascale and Millom Rural District might have experienced unusually high incidence rates of leukaemia in young people. However, the findings are based on small numbers of cases. Excesses of cancer over the levels expected were also reported in Carlisle and Wigton among people under the age of 25 years during 1959–67 (Gardner and Winter 1984), and we are aware of leukaemia 'clusters' reported in other areas of the country, not all in the neighbourhood of nuclear plants. It was thus important to compare the rates in Seascale and Millom Rural District with levels in similar communities throughout the region and country to enable us to assess how unusual such increased rates may be.

2.35 Dr A. Craft used the Northern Children's Cancer Registry to calculate cancer and leukaemia incidence rates among under 15 year-olds for each of the 765 electoral wards in the region (Craft and Openshaw, 1984). He estimated that the Registry contained more than 98% of the 0–14 year old cases of childhood cancer occurring in the catchment area. He was able to use incidence rather than death certificate data, an increasingly important point now that therapy for childhood leukaemia has improved and a significant proportion of the patients survive for many years. These data are available for 1968–82. The expected rates used to calculate Standardised Mortality Ratios (SMRs) are based on population figures from the 1981 Census. This could be a source of error, since the size and age distribution of the under 15 year old populations of the wards in earlier years might have been different. For example, the childhood populations of Seascale, the 5 coastal parishes and the rest of Millom Rural District in the last 3 Censuses are shown in Tables 2.17 and Figure 2.4. Thus, although an over-estimation of the risk in

Table 2.17 Childhood Population of Seascale, the 5 coastal parishes and the rest of Millom Rural District in the 1961, 1971 and 1981 Censuses

	Area	1961 Census	1971 Census	1981 Census
0–14 Year old Population	Seascale	606	603	411
	5 Coastal Parishes	1,275	1,085	741
	Rest of Millom Rural District	2,623	2,278	1,849

(Palmer, 1984)

Seascale could be occurring, there is evidence for a similar decline in the young population in adjacent areas over the years. The change of population numbers under 15 years of age in other more distant wards of the region is not known. Dr Craft intends to recalculate incidence rates incorporating earlier census figures to provide a more accurate assessment.

2.36 In this study of 765 electoral wards Seascale ranked sixth highest in incidence rates for all childhood cancers (Table 2.18). The rate in Seascale,

Table 2.18 Ranking of cancer incidence rate per 1,000 children—top ten of 765 electoral wards in Northern Region

Ward Rank Order	Number of Cancer Cases	Population 0–14 years	Rate/1,000 Children	Poisson Probability	Ward Incidence Regional Incidence
1	2	97	20·61	0·012877	11·78
2	2	133	13·88	0·026891	7·93
3	2	165	12·12	0·034471	6·92
4	2	183	10·92	0·041544	6·24
5	3	281	10·67	0·013771	6·10
6*	4	411	9·73	0·006318	5·56
7	6	676	8·87	0·001397	5·07
8	2	231	8·65	0·062698	4·94
9	8	953	8·39	0·000342	4·79
10	5	605	8·26	0·004643	4·72

*Seascale   (Craft and Openshaw, 1984)

although based on only four cases, is statistically significantly raised (p=0·006) above the regional incidence by an estimated factor of between 5 and 6 fold. When the wards with the highest rates were plotted on a map, no obvious goegraphical pattern emerged.

Figure 2.4 Percentage of children 0—14 in Seascale, 5 Coastal Parishes and Rest of Millom RD in 1971 and 1961 Census data relative to 1981 Census data.

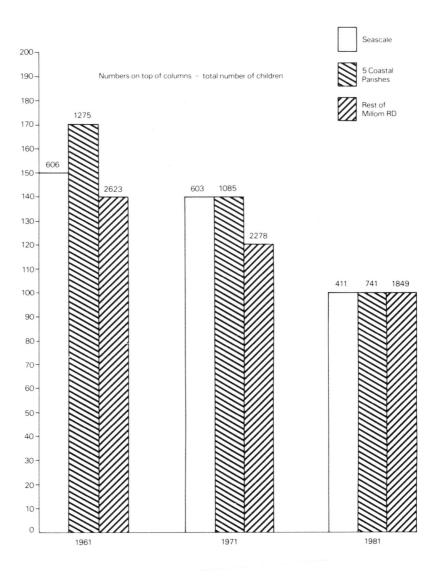

(Palmer, 1984)

2.37 For the years studied, Seascale had the third highest incidence rate of childhood 'lymphoid malignancy' among the 765 electoral wards (Table 2.19). Again the rate in Seascale is based on (the same) 4 cases, but is

Table 2.19 Ranking of lymphoid malignancy incidence rate per 1,000 children—top ten of 765 electoral wards in Northern Region

Ward Rank Order	Number of cases	Child Population	Rate/1,000 Children	Poisson Probability	Ward Incidence Regional Incidence
1	2	144	13·88	0·003622	22·82
2	1	97	10·30	0·057317	16·94
3*	4	411	9·73	0·000134	15·99
4	1	165	6·06	0·095528	9·96
5	1	172	5·81	0·099373	9·55
6	1	174	5·74	0·100468	9·44
7	1	184	5·43	0·105925	8·93
8	1	189	5·29	0·108641	8·69
9	1	198	5·05	0·113510	8·30
10	1	203	4·92	0·116203	8·09

*Seascale   (Craft and Openshaw, 1984)

statistically significantly ($p=0\cdot0001$) raised over the regional level by a factor of about 16. If the population of under-15 year-olds is taken as the high figure of 606 for the whole period (1961 Census data, Table 2.17), the estimated incidence rate in Seascale is still higher than the fourth ranking ward. Again there was no tendency for wards with higher rates to be in West Cumbria rather than in other parts of the Northern Region.

2.38 Comparisons with other areas were also carried out by Gardner and Winter (1984b), who examined leukaemia mortality among young people under the age of 25 years in each of the 469 Rural Districts in England and Wales during 1968–78. They found 7 with statistically significant raised leukaemia death rates in the under 25 year-old group. This is fewer than might be expected (about 12) to occur by chance if the underlying rates were the same in all areas, and the observed differences were due only to the limited number of calendar years and hence limited numbers of deaths studied. Millom Rural District, however, had the second highest rate out of 152 similar sized Rural Districts (Table 2.20).

Table 2.20 Distribution of mortality from leukaemia under 25 years of age in 152 rural districts of England and Wales of similar size to Millom Rural District*

Standardised Mortality Ratio (SMR)	Number of Rural Districts*	
	Observed	Predicted
0–	35	35·7
50–	43	50·2
100–	26	25·9
150–	26	22·5
200–	14	9·2
250–	5	5·4
300–	1	1·8
350–	0	0·9
400+	2	0·4
Total	152	152

*Similar-sized Rural Districts are those with an expected number of leukaemia deaths of between 1 and 2 in persons aged 0–24 years during 1968–78. Millom Rural District had an expected number of 1·4 deaths, but 6 deaths were recorded giving an SMR of 435. This value is the second highest in the Observed column of this Table.
+Observed=SMRs as they occurred; Predicted=SMRs as predicted on the basis of a Poisson distribution for each Rural District with its specific expected number of deaths.

(Gardner and Winter, 1984b)

2.39 Gardner and Winter also considered the distribution of mortality rates that would be expected among the 152 Rural Districts of a similar size to Millom Rural District if they all had the same underlying leukaemia age-specific death rates in young people under the age of 25 years. Because of the limited time period studied, from 1968–78, the expected numbers of deaths were between 1 and 2 in each of the Rural Districts—the expected number in Millom Rural District being 1·4. Assuming that the number of observed deaths in each Rural District followed a Poisson distribution, Table 2.20 shows the comparison of the observed and predicted distributions*. It can be seen that they are not very different overall, which is confirmed by a formal statistical test. Millom Rural District, as said above, had the second highest mortality rate, being one of the two areas with an SMR over 400 compared with the 0·4 areas predicted.

2.40 It is important to note that in neither of the latter two studies were the rates in the areas of interest (Seascale and Millom Rural District) above the observed range, but they were close to the top. Thus, the Seascale incidence and Millom Rural District mortality rates for leukaemia among young people are unusual, though not unparalleled.

2.41 It has already been mentioned that the discharges from Sellafield are much larger than those from other nuclear plants around the country (paragraph 1.10). We are aware of work in progress on the incidence of leukaemia and cancer around other nuclear power stations in England and Wales but none was completed in time for us to consider in our report.

OTHER DATA

(i) Scottish Data

2.42 A report by Heasman et al (1984) was made available to us. The study showed a statistically significantly higher registration rate for myeloid leukaemia (p<0.05) in the 0–24 year old group between 1968–74 on the West Coast of Scotland, but this was diminished during 1975–81. There was a lower registration rate for lymphoid leukaemia during the earlier period, and while the registration rate for all leukaemias was higher on the West Coast than in the rest of Scotland, this excess did not reach statistical significance. While it is possible that the excess of myeloid cases was due to incorrect coding, registration or diagnosis, there is obviously need for further investigation of this matter and we understand that this is now being undertaken.

(ii) Down's Syndrome in Maryport Town

2.43 While we were preparing this report the Daily Mirror reported that 4 women born in the same street in Maryport all subsequently had children with Down's Syndrome (Foot P. 1984a). Later a further 4 cases of Down's Syndrome in the children of mothers living in Maryport were reported (Foot 1984b, Foot 1984c). There was also a suggestion that several cases of Down's Syndrome in Eire might be related to discharges from Sellafield (Sheehan and Hillary, 1983). To interpret these data it is clearly necessary to have more details of the population from which these groups are drawn. Apart from the fact that this subject fell outside our terms of reference, its proper assessment would require detailed studies of maternal age-specific rates of congenital disease. Such an investigation was not feasible in the time available. Recognising these concerns we have, however, made a recommendation for further research at the end of this Chapter.

---

*There is a well-known statistical result stating that when a small number of events are shared out without bias the numbers in each share differ according to a formula, the Poisson distribution. This formula can be used to test whether an observed distribution of events is more variable than could be explained by chance (eg the numbers of leukaemia cases in Rural Districts of England and Wales).

DISCUSSION

2.44 Seascale had the third highest incidence rate of lymphoid malignancy in under 15 year-olds among 765 electoral wards in the region covered by the Northern Children's Cancer Registry between 1968–82, and Millom Rural District had the second highest death rate from leukaemia in under 25 year-olds among 152 similar-sized Rural Districts between 1968–78 throughout England and Wales. This does not necessarily mean that radio-active waste discharged from the Sellafield site into the atmosphere and sea nearby is the cause of the increase. The effect of chance or some other unidentified cause cannot be excluded, and the fact that the other electoral wards and Rural Districts with increased rates were geographically scattered outside the area around Sellafield is relevant here.

2.45 In the electoral ward study the number of leukaemia cases registered in each ward was necessarily small because of the rarity of the disease, the small size of electoral wards, and the limited time period of observation. In Seascale there were four cases during 1968–82, and in Millom Rural District there were 6 leukaemia deaths in Millom Rural District during 1968–78. Even though the above studies are based on small numbers, nevertheless they are consistent in demonstrating a higher incidence of leukaemia in young people resident in the area.

2.46 Most cases of childhood leukaemia are of unknown cause, and therefore caution is necessary in interpreting the results described above. An observed association between two factors does not prove a causal relationship. Some third, possibly unthought of factor might be the cause. We have already seen that Seascale is not a typical West Cumbrian village. It has been suggested to us that such factors as the consumption of unpasteurised milk and the discharge of untreated sewage into the sea may be relevant. But there is no scientific evidence that these are important in the aetiology of childhood leukaemia. Radiation is the only established environmental cause of leukaemia in children within the limits of present knowledge. While there is evidence that radiation-induced leukaemia in adults usually results in myeloid leukaemia, there is not known to be such an association of myeloid histology with radiation-induced childhood leukaemia.

2.47 In the Annex to Chapter 3 and in Chapter 4 we will look at the environmental features of the area to see whether radiation exposure or exposure to any other environmental factor is likely to be contributory to this high incidence.

RECOMMENDATIONS FOR FURTHER EPIDEMILOGICAL RESEARCH

2.48 Having reviewed the epidemiological evidence available we feel the following studies could provide additional information.

Case-control study

2.49 We recommend that a case-control study to investigate relevant features of the records on cases of leukaemia and lymphoma which have been diagnosed in young people under the age of 25 years in the West Cumbria Health Authority area since 1950 should be undertaken. The intention would be to compare them with a control group of young people—appropriately selected—who have not developed leukaemia or lymphoma. We suggest that both leukaemias and lymphomas be studied because there are sometimes difficulties in differentiating between these two diseases, and we would exclude other childhood cancers because the evidence for any excess of these in the area is less strong.

2.50 We recognise there will be many difficulties in setting up a study of this kind, covering a 30 year period and based on index cases many of whom will have died. Nevertheless, we believe it is important to investigate the possibility of studying the index cases in more detail than has yet been done.

2.51 We have been involved in discussions with the Department of Health and Social Security about this study, and the initial work is in hand.

Birth cohort study

2.52 We recommend that a study be carried out on the records of all children born since 1950 to mothers resident in Seascale at the time of birth to examine cancer incidence and mortality (i.e., a birth cohort study).

2.53 The routine analysis of leukaemia incidence and mortality data using currently available statistics is restricted to people developing cancer while resident in an area. However, given the mobility of the population, this approach has limitations. A birth cohort study would identify all cases of cancer diagnosed among children born in Seascale, even after they have left the area.

2.54 Preparations for this study have commenced, and a list of births to mothers resident in Seascale between 1950–1983 is being compiled. This list will form the basis of the birth cohort study.

School studies

2.55 The registers for some local schools are available. The feasibility of using this information to trace records on the children and to establish the incidence of cancer among them should be examined.

Further work using the cancer registries

2.56 Dr Craft's study on cancer incidence in the 765 electoral wards in the catchment area of the Northern Children's Cancer Registry has already been mentioned. Because of the short time available to Dr Craft to complete this study in time for our report, the number of children at risk was based on those resident in the electoral wards and under 15 years of age in the 1981 Census. We are aware that the population of Seascale has fluctuated over the last 30 years, and do not know how the populations of other electoral wards in the area have fluctuated in this period.

2.57 We recommend that Dr Craft should be asked to extend his calculations using 1961, 1971 and 1981 Census population data where appropriate. It may also be useful if the data could be recorded to include place of residence at birth as well as at diagnosis.

2.58 Childhood leukaemia is more common under the age of five, and if the proportion of children under the age of five was excessively large in Seascale compared to the national figure, this could result in an apparent excess of cases in the 0–14 year-old age group.

2.59 We recommend that cancer incidence by electoral ward in the Northern Children's Cancer Registry area be standardised for age at diagnosis in order to determine whether the excess of leukaemia in Seascale might be related to any unusual features of the age distribution of the children there.

Down's Syndrome

2.60 Preliminary data from the area (Dr Terrell, 1984) suggest an incidence of Down's Syndrome for Maryport of 1 in 660 from 1968–1983. This figure is not much different from the expected population incidence of 1 in 600 births (Mikkelsen M, 1981). We know of no cases of Down's Syndrome occurring in Seascale itself, not is there any suggestion of a high incidence in other surrounding areas. However, because the incidence of Down's Syndrome is strongly related to maternal age and because total ascertainment of cases requires the collation of multiple sources, these data must all be regarded as preliminary.

2.61 The evidence on whether parental irradiation causes chromosomal aneuploidies such as Down's Syndrome is conflicting (reviewed by Bond DJ and Chandley AC, 1983). There was no detectable increase in the condition amongst the survivors in Japan of the atom bombs. Among 12 studies which have been published examining the history of medical radiation exposure in mothers of cases there are conflicting results. The majority of these studies do, however, suggest a detectable positive relationship which does not always achieve statistical significance.

2.62 Given that there is, therefore, some reason for believing that parental irradiation may be a cause of chromosomal anomalies such as Down's Syndrome, we recommend that a detailed study to determine the maternal age-specific frequency of congenital chromosomal disorders in the vicinity of Sellafield should be undertaken.

References

Alderson M R, Ashwood F L, and Cook-Mozaffari P (1984) Mortality and Cancer Registrations in the vicinity of nuclear installations in England and Wales. Submission to Black Advisory Group, (SDB 596/H24).

Bond D J and Chandley A C (1983) Oxford Monographs on Medical Genetics *11* Aneuploidy; Oxford University University Press.

Boyd J T, Doll R, Faulds J S and Leiper J (1970) Cancer of the lung in Iron ore (haematite) miners. Br J Ind Med *27* (2) 97–105.

Clough E A (1983) Further Report on the BNFL Radiation Mortality Study. J Soc Radiol Prot *3* (3) 18–20 (SDB 26/I2).

Cook-Mozaffari P (1984) Deaths from cancer in South Coastal Cumbria (Copeland District). Submission to Black Advisory Group (SDB 587/H13).

Craft A W and Birch J M (1983) Childhood Cancer in Cumbria. Lancet, December 3rd, 1299 (SDB 532/H21).

Craft A W and Openshaw S (1984) Childhood Cancer in Northern Region, 1968–82. Personal communication to Sir Douglas Black (SDB 555/H21).

J Cutler (1983a) Young Leukaemia Cases in Seascale. Personal communication to Sir Douglas Black (Report 2, SDB 178/I1/P1).

J Cutler (1983b) Childhood Cancer near Windscale. Statement to the Black Advisory Group, 12th December 1983 (SDB 177/I1/P1).

Faulds J S and Stewart M J (1956) Carcinoma of the lung in haematite miners. J Path Bact *72* 353–366.

Foot P (1984a) Just Coincidence, Daily Mirror, February 9th 1984, p4 (SDB 709/C6).

Foot P (1984b) Coincidence Strikes again, Daily Mirror, February 23rd 1984, (SDB 709/C6).

Foot P (1984c) Riddle of the sands, Daily Mirror, April 19th 1984, (SDB 709/C6).

Gardner M J and Winter P D, (1984a) Cancer in Cumberland during 1959–68 with reference to cancer in young people around Windscale. Lancet, 24 January 1984 (SDB 334/H4).

Gardner and Winter (1984b) Further analysis of leukaemia in young people in Rural Districts of England and Wales (SDB 345/H10; SDB 400/H10).

Gardner M J, Winter T D, Taylor C P and Acheson E D (1983) Atlas of Cancer Mortality in England and Wales, Wiley.

Heasman M A, Kemp I W, MacLaren A M et al. (1984) Incidence of leukaemia in young persons in the West of Scotland. Lancet May 26, 1984 188–1189 (EV7).

Mikkelsen M (1981 in Trisomy 21, Burgio G R, Fraccaro M, Tiepolo L, and Wolf U eds p 211, Springer Verlag.

Palmer M K (1984) Deaths from cancer at ages under 25 in 5 coastal parishes compared with the rest of Millom Rural District, 1963–80. Submission to Black Advisory Group (SDB 588/H28).

Sheehan P M E and Hillary I B (1983) An unusual cluster of babies with Down's Syndrome born to former pupils of an Irish Boarding School. Brit Med J *287* 1428–1429.

Stevenson M D and Walker B (1984) The incidence of acute childhood leukaemia in Seascale, Cumbria. Submission to Black Advisory Group (SDB 442/P2).

Terrell J D, Down's Syndrome in West Cumbria. Submission to Black Advisory Group (SDB 443/I6/P4).

Tiplady P (1981; 1983) Leukaemia and other Cancers in Cumbria. Submission to Black Advisory Group, Appendix A (SDB 254/I6).

J Urquhart (1983) Young Cancer Cases in Millom, West Cumbria. Personal Communication to Sir Douglas Black (Report 2, SDB 178/I1/P1).

Urquhart J, Palmer M and Cutler J (1984) Cancer in Cumbria: the Windscale connection. Lancet, 24 January (SDB 335/H4).

CHAPTER 3

SOME ENVIRONMENTAL ASPECTS OF THE SELLAFIELD SITE AND ITS RELATIONSHIP TO THE NUCLEAR POWER INDUSTRY IN THE UNITED KINGDOM*

INTRODUCTION

3.1 A summary of the main features of nuclear reactors and of the scientific background to the generation of power from nuclear fuel is contained in Chapter Three of the Royal Commission on Environmental Pollution (RCEP) Sixth Report: Nuclear Power and the Environment, published in 1976. The background material presented here was derived in part from that Report, and has been updated with data provided by British Nuclear Fuels plc (BNFL), the National Radiological Protection Board (NRPB), the Electricity Boards and relevant Government Departments where necessary. We have not critically assessed all the information in this chapter, which is provided largely to facilitate understanding of the following chapter.

3.2 The civil use of nuclear power to generate electricity commenced in the United Kingdom (UK) with the development of magnox reactors in the 1950s. In the 1970's the first Advanced Gas-Cooled Reactors were commissioned. Nuclear establishments in the United Kingdom are shown in Figure 3.1.

3.3 The 'nuclear fuel cycle' includes all operations involved in the fabrication and treatment of nuclear fuel, and is represented in simplified form in Figure 3.2. Sellafield is the nuclear site in the UK where spent fuel from nuclear power stations is reprocessed. There is a smaller scale reprocessing operation at Dounreay, which deals with fuel from fast breeder reactors.

---

*The Annex to Chapter 3 deals with non-radiation related environmental aspects of Cumbria.

Figure 3.1 Nuclear establishments in the U.K. (Exludes M.O.D. sites)

KEY

▲ CEGB Power stations
△ SSEB Power stations
■ UKAEA Research establishments
● BNF plc sites
◆ Amersham International plc sites

DOUNREAY
TORNESS △
HUNTERSTON
CHAPELCROSS
HARTLEPOOL
WINDSCALE
CALDER HALL &
SELLAFIELD
HEYSHAM
SPRINGFIELDS
WYLFA
RISLEY
CULCHETH
CAPENHURST
TRAWSFYNYDD
SIZEWELL
BERKELEY
CARDIFF
CULHAM
AMERSHAM
BRADWELL
OLDBURY
HARWELL
HINKLEY POINT
DUNGENESS
WINFRITH

Figure 3.2 The nuclear fuel cycle

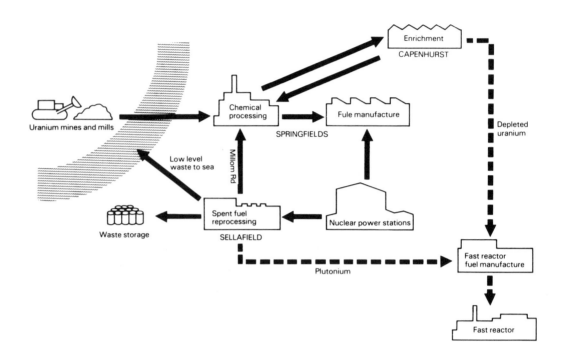

(adapted from a BNFL diagram)

THE SELLAFIELD SITE

3.4 The Sellafield site is located in West Cumbria near the coast. It was acquired in 1947 for the production of plutonium for defence purposes. Two nuclear reactors and a spent fuel reprocessing plant were in operation by 1952. Responsibility for the site was transferred from the Ministry of Supply to the United Kingdom Atomic Energy Authority (UKAEA) when it was formed in 1954 and subsequently transferred to BNFL when that company was formed in 1971. The various stages of development of the site are set out in Table 3.1

Table 3.1   **Stages in the development of the Sellafield site**

	Date Operational	Date Shut down
Site available July 1947	Work commenced Sept 1947	—
First and Second Pipeline to Sea	Laid June 1950	—
No. 1 Pile	Critical Oct 1950	Oct 1957
No. 2 Pile	Critical June 1951	Oct 1957
First Reprocessing Plant and Associated Facilities	Jan 1952 et seq.	Reprocessing Plant converted to Head End Plant for oxide fuel and used 1969 to 1973
First Calder Hall Reactor	Aug 1956	—
All Calder Hall Reactors	1958	—
Prototype Advanced Gas-Cooled Reactor	1963	April 1981
Second Reprocessing Plant and Associated Facilities (magnox fuel)	1964 et seq.	—
Spent Oxide Fuel Storage Plant	1968 et seq.	—
Prototype Fast Reactor Fuel Fabrication Plant	1970	—
Third Pipeline to Sea	Laid 1976	—

3.5 Reprocessing of magnox fuel from nuclear power stations around the country and from power stations at Latina in Italy and Tokai Mura in Japan takes place at the Windscale reprocessing plant situated on the Sellafield site. The site is also used for the storage of oxide fuel from the UK advanced gas cooled reactors and from overseas. There is also a plant for fabricating fuel for the UKAEA prototype fast reactor and there are 4 nuclear power reactors (Calder Hall) (Table 3.2). About 7 kilometres south of Sellafield on the coast at Drigg there is an authorised disposal site for low level radioactive waste, also owned and operated by BNFL.

Table 3.2 **Sellafield Site—principal civil functions 1983**

1. Receipt, storage and reprocessing of spent magnox fuel
2. Treatment and storage of products of processing
3. Receipt and storage of spent oxide fuel
4. Fabrication and storage of plutonium fuel elements for fast breeder reactors
5. Operation of Calder Hall reactors
6. Treatment and storage or disposal of waste products
7. UKAEA Research Laboratory

3.6 The nuclear component of the present energy supply of the United Kingdom depends on Sellafield (Figure 3.2). Nuclear power stations send their spent fuel to Sellafield either for reprocessing (if they use magnox fuel), or for storage (if they use zirconium-clad or stainless steel clad fuel). Facilities for on-site storage of spent fuel at power stations throughout the country are limited and if facilities for accepting spent fuel at Sellafield were to cease for any reason, then in due course the nuclear power stations would cease to function until further arrangements could be made for the storage of spent fuel.

RELATIONSHIP BETWEEN ON-SITE OPERATIONS AND DISCHARGES

3.7 It is important to differentiate between airborne and liquid discharges due to reprocessing and airborne and liquid discharges from a nuclear power station producing electricity. Figure 1.1 shows the magnitude of the collective dose commitments assessed by NRPB for the general public from discharges from different sites in the UK permitted to release radioactivity into the environment. The contribution from Sellafield is assessed to be far greater than that from any other site in the UK. For the purpose of this report we have assumed that the radiological risk arising from nuclear power operations in areas adjacent to other nuclear sites is likely to be substantially less than that in areas adjacent to Sellafield.

3.8 The discharges of radioactive waste from Sellafield arise from a variety of operations giving rise to particular combinations of isotypes—of differing radiobiological significance—which vary from time to time. BNFL told us that UK population exposure arises mainly from past and present liquid discharges from irradiated fuel storage and from reprocessing. Figure 3.3 shows the 'total alpha' and Figure 3.4 the 'total beta' liquid discharges since 1980 with BNFL's forward projections until the year 2000 based on their plans as announced up to October 1983. The projections are based on oxide fuel reprocessing in the Thermal Oxide Reprocessing Plant (THORP), commencing in 1990 and on both magnox and oxide fuel reprocessing continuing at least until the year 2000. BNFL announced in June 1984 that it is studying how quickly the discharges to sea could be reduced to as near zero as possible. The scheme to be implemented will be decided after discussions with Government Departments and regulatory bodies.

Figure 3.3 Annual total beta discharges to sea from Sellafield (Figure supplied by BNFL)

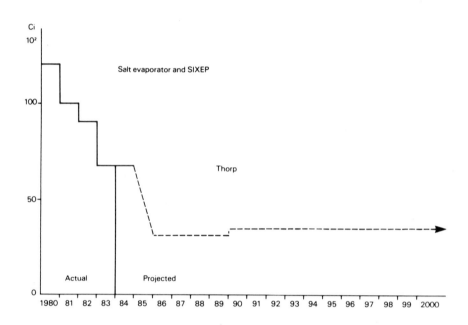

Figure 3.4 Annual total alpha discharges to sea from Sellafield (Figure supplied by BNFL)

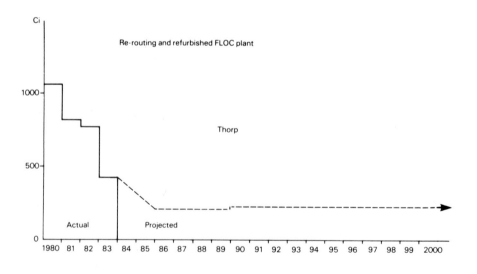

3.9 The defence programme determined operations at—and therefore radioactive discharges from—the Sellafield site in its early years. The requirements of the civil nuclear power programme arose in the 1960's and have now become dominant. We were told by BNFL that at present approximately 70% of the 'total alpha' and 70% of the 'total beta' liquid discharge is attributable to storage and reprocessing of magnox fuel from Central Electricity Generating Board (CEGB) and South of Scotland Electricity Board (SSEB) nuclear power stations, and around 10% to reprocessing magnox fuel from overseas. About $1\frac{1}{2}$% of liquid discharges is due to on-site storage of oxide fuel from UK nuclear power stations and a further 3% from storage of oxide fuel from overseas stations.

3.10 The Ministry of Defence (MOD) and BNFL have informed us, as an indicator of the potential significance of defence activities, that the operation of Calder Hall and Chapelcross nuclear power stations (for which MOD can request a change in the mode of operation to produce plutonium for defence purposes) has been responsible for about 15% of the liquid discharges from Sellafield over the past ten years. MOD and BNFL have also informed us that the radio-isotypes arising from meeting defence requirements have not differed from those arising from civil operations except in the case of Polonium in the early years. In their assessment of population exposure arising from Sellafield discharges, NRPB have taken account of this, and in particular of the accidental release of Polonium to the atmosphere in 1957 which occurred due to the increased temperatures reached during the Windscale fire.

DESCRIPTION OF FUEL REPROCESSING*

3.11 Magnox fuel has to be reprocessed to avoid the consequences of its corrosion when stored under water for longer than about two years. Reprocessing also permits Uranium and Plutonium to be recovered thus reducing the need for Uranium ore. Spent fuel from the nuclear power stations is initially stored at the power stations while its radioactivity decays to a level which permits its transport to Sellafield. It is then transported by British Rail in steel flasks (crash-resistant containers specially designed to tranport the fuel to Sellafield). BNFL told us that a small amount of spent fuel travels by road from Chapelcross. Fuel from abroad arrives by ship at Barrow, from where it is transported by British Rail to Sellafield. The spent fuel is placed in cooling ponds on arrival at Sellafield to await reprocessing. We understand that after the magnox fuel has been stored in water for about two years corrosion of the magnesium alloy containing the Uranium leads to corrosion of Uranium and release of fission products into the water. For this reason reprocessing should normally take place promptly so that total residence time in the ponds is less than about two years. The enforced cessation of reprocessing in 1973/4, due to a number of factors including the industrial relations problems widespread throughout UK industry at the time, increased pond stocks and residence time. As a consequence there were enhanced radiation levels for the workforce and enhanced discharges, primarily of Caesium isotopes, which were the source of the peak site discharges in 1974 and 1975. Discharges and pond stocks have been substantially reduced since then but the beta discharges from the site are still dominated by those arising from the magnox storage ponds. BNFL's forward projections (Figures 3.3 and 3.4) recognise the further reductions which are expected with the availability of new plant.

*Information in this section came from BNFL and the RCEP 6th Report.

3.12 Up to some 1,500 tonnes of irradiated magnox fuel is reprocessed at Sellafield each year and about 1,100 tonnes of irradiated magnox fuel is at present stored on site awaiting reprocessing.

3.13 Spent fuel from nuclear reactors other than magnox is either clad in zirconium or stainless steel. This does not corrode as rapidly as magnox fuel and can thus be kept for much longer periods in the cooling ponds. At present about 1,200 tonnes of spent oxide fuel from overseas is stored on site together with about 350 tonnes of UK spent oxide fuel. None of this spent fuel will be reprocessed until the Thermal Oxide Reprocessing Plant (THORP) is completed in 1990 (Table 3.3)

Table 3.3 **Major new plant at present under construction at the Sellafield site**

	Operational
1. New spent fuel storage and decanning complex	Phased from early 1985
2. Site Ion Exchange Effluent Treatment Plant (SIXEP)	Early 1985
3. Salt Evaporator Effluent Treatment Plant	Early 1985
4. Waste Treatment Complex	1988
5. Vitrification plant for high activity liquid waste	1988
6. Thermal Oxide Reprocessing Plant (THORP)	1990

3.14 Magnox power stations are no longer being built, but we were told that those presently in use could have an anticipated further life of 8 to 15 years. Therefore it is expected that there will be a need to reprocess magnox fuel at Sellafield up to about the year 2000.

MANAGEMENT OF RADIOACTIVE WASTE

3.15 After reprocessing, all radioactive products except low activity waste are stored on site, and therefore need not be considered further in this report. Some low activity waste is discharged to sea (liquid) to atmosphere (gaseous) or sent to the Drigg Site (where solid material is buried in trenches) subject to the authorisation under the Radioactive Substances Act 1960.

3.16 Low level liquid waste is discharged to sea via pipelines crossing the railway line and the river Ehen to discharge 2·1 kilometres to seaward of the low tide line.

3.17 Gaseous wastes consist largely of inert gases and Iodine. They may contain particulate material which could leave the site as part of airborne emissions, and therefore high efficiency particle absorbers (HEPA) are installed where appropriate.

3.18* The International Commission on Radiological Protection (ICRP) has issued guidance on the control of occupational and public exposure to radiation with the exception of natural and medical exposures. These recommendations form the basis of a European Directive on Radiation Protection and have been endorsed by the NRPB. In summary, the dose equivalent to members of the public should be limited both by complying with a dose limit and by keeping all doses as low as reasonably achievable (ALARA), economic and social factors being taken into account. The dose limit relates to the sum of the annual effective dose equivalent from external irradiation and the committed effective dose equivalent from intake of radioactive materials in the same year. It is to be applied to the average member of the 'critical group'. A 'critical group' is a term applied to those people in the exposed population, generally only few in number, who are likely to receive the highest levels of dose. Because 'critical groups' are

*Paragraphs 3.18–3.21 were largely provided by NRPB.

exposed at a higher level than the rest of the population they are chosen to be relatively homogeneous with respect to characteristics that affect the doses received. The currently recommended dose limit is 5 mSv (500 mrem) in a year. The effect of the additional requirement to keep all doses as low as reasonably achievable and of the widespread use of maximising assumptions in assessing the dose equivalent actually received by members of 'critical groups' is such as to make it very likely that the average dose equivalent over a lifetime to a member of a 'critical group' is no more than 1 mSv in a year. The NRPB would expect the control of radioactive wastes to be such as to achieve this long-term average and thus the corresponding lifetime dose equivalent of 70 mSv.

3.19 The additional risk of death for a group of men and women uniformly exposed over a lifetime at an average level of 1 mSv in a year would be estimated to rise from zero in the first few years to about 1 in 10^5 per year (1 in 100,000) after several decades. The average additional risk of death to the whole populations for which the 'critical groups' represent the highly exposed sub-groups is believed to be less than 1 in 10^6 per year (1 in a million) (ICRP 26).

3.20 Since it is not possible to measure a committed dose equivalent directly, both ICRP and NRPB provide secondary limits expressed as annual limits of intake in becquerels (curies) per year. These can be further developed to give derived limits, eg for the concentration of radioactive materials in a foodstuff such as fish or milk. These derived limits are then specific to a 'critical group' of known habits and food consumption in a known environment, although generalised derived limits covering any reasonable behaviour patterns and environmental conditions can also be developed. These secondary and derived limits are appropriate as a basis for control procedures. Since they are based on specific metabolic models and organ sizes and on representative factors relating dose equivalent to risk at all ages and for both sexes, they should be used with discretion when estimating the consequences of exposure of individuals or small groups who may not be representative of the more general groups for which the limits were intended.

3.21 Occupational exposure limits are set at 10 times the level for exposure of the public. This is based on an ICRP estimate of the annual risk of death of 10^{-2} per Sv (10^{-4} per rem), which produces a radiation risk which is comparable to the fatal accident risk in an 'averagely safe' industry. So far no change in cancer mortality or in the incidence of any other disease has been demonstrated in such workers at Sellafield (Clough, 1983) though we are aware of further studies in progress.

3.22 The ICRP recommendations are given in terms of the dose actually received by members of the public in any one year from external radiation and intakes of radionuclides, plus any dose that will be received during the life of the individual from radionuclides retained in the body beyond the year in question. Measurements of levels of radioactivity in fish, meat and the environment are made in becquerels (curies) per unit mass or volume of material sampled. To calculate exposure from the monitoring data it is therefore necessary to know:—

    i. the amount of the radioactive material that will come into contact with the person over a given period of time via all possible pathways (eg inhalation, ingestion, contact);

    ii. how much of the material will remain in the body, how much will be excreted and over what period of time, (this usually involves an assessment of the 'biological half-life' of the material);

iii. in which tissues or organs the radioactive material taken into the body will be preferentially concentrated;

iv. the rate of radioactive decay of the radionuclide;

v. the type of radiation emitted, ie alpha, beta or gamma radiation, and the energy of the radiation emitted, so that some assessment of the amount of tissue irradiated can be made.

3.23 A more detailed assessment of the assumptions made in the calculation of population exposure from monitoring results will be found in Chapter 4.

3.24 Before the pipeline authorisation was made in 1952, investigations of the sea currents and likely biological pathways by which discharges might give rise to population doses were carried out, (Dunster, 1956; Dunster, 1958; Seligman, 1956; Fair and Maclean, 1956). These studies formed the basis of the initial, very conservative authorisation in February 1952 (Wix et al, 1960). Monitoring of the sea food and of the environment since then has continued and become increasingly more detailed. We were told that the present MAFF marine monitoring programme has an annual budget of around half a million pounds. The monitoring programme is dealt with in more detail in Chapter 4.

3.25 The present limits for liquid discharges from the Sellafield site are authorised jointly by the Department of the Environment and the Ministry of Agriculture, Fisheries and Food (MAFF). The authorisation deals separately with alpha and beta emitters, and provides upper limits for discharges over three monthly periods, with further overall limits on annual discharges permitted. At present discharges of $2 \cdot 78 \times 10^{15}$ Bq (75,000 Ci) of 'total beta' emitters, taken together, and 74×10^{12} Bq (2,000 Ci) of 'total alpha' emitters are permitted in each consecutive 3 month period. There is an overall limit of 222×10^{12} Bq (6,000 Ci) on 'total alpha' discharges per annum, and limits on the amounts of Ruthenium-106, Strontium-90 and Cerium-144 permitted within the 'total beta' authorisation. Limit on the discharge of Caesium-137 is via the beta limit and the 'as low as reasonably achievable' (ALARA) clause (see para 3.18). There is no limit on the authorisation for Plutonium-241 or Tritium, both of which are very low energy beta emitters, but these discharges are measured and the quantities published in BNFL's annual report.

3.26 The present authorisation dates from 1971, when the authorised limit for 'total alpha' discharges were amended following an expected increase in workload. At that time environmental monitoring suggested that the environmental levels of radiation from the discharges resulted in levels of radiation exposures to the public within the ICRP recommended dose limits.

3.27 In February 1983 the authorisation was varied to formally require BNFL to keep all discharges 'as low as reasonably achievable' (ALARA) although it had been the practise for a number of years before this for this principle to operate (eg the placing of zeolite resin skips in the cooling ponds to reduce Caesium-137 discharges was required by the authorising department on these grounds). 'Total beta' discharges for 1983 were less than $2 \cdot 5 \times 10^{15}$ Bq (67,200 Ci) and 'total alpha' discharges were 14×10^{12} Bq (378 Ci) which are some 22% and 6% respectively of the authorised limits.

3.28 Figures 3.5, 3.6, 3.7 and 3.8 show the pattern of liquid discharges since they commenced. Peak discharges of beta activity, $9 \cdot 2 \times 10^{15}$ Bq (245,000 Ci) took place in 1975 and included $6 \cdot 3 \times 10^{15}$ Bq (170,000 Ci) of Caesium isotopes. Peak alpha activity discharges were $1 \cdot 8 \times 10^{14}$ Bq (4,900 Ci) per annum in 1973.

Figure 3.5 Discharges to sea of 'total alpha' activity from Sellafield site (Figure supplied by BNFL)

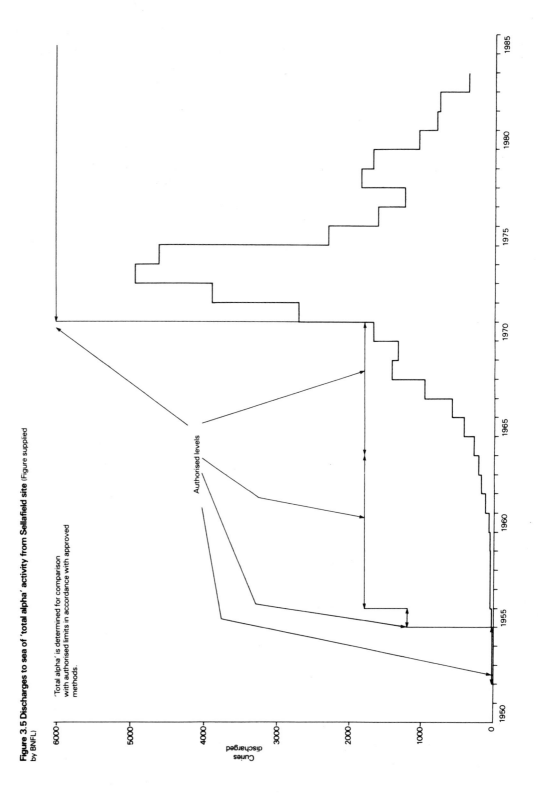

'Total alpha' is determined for comparison with authorised limits in accordance with approved methods.

Figure 3.6 Discharges of 'total beta' activity to sea from Sellafield site (Figure supplied by BNFL)

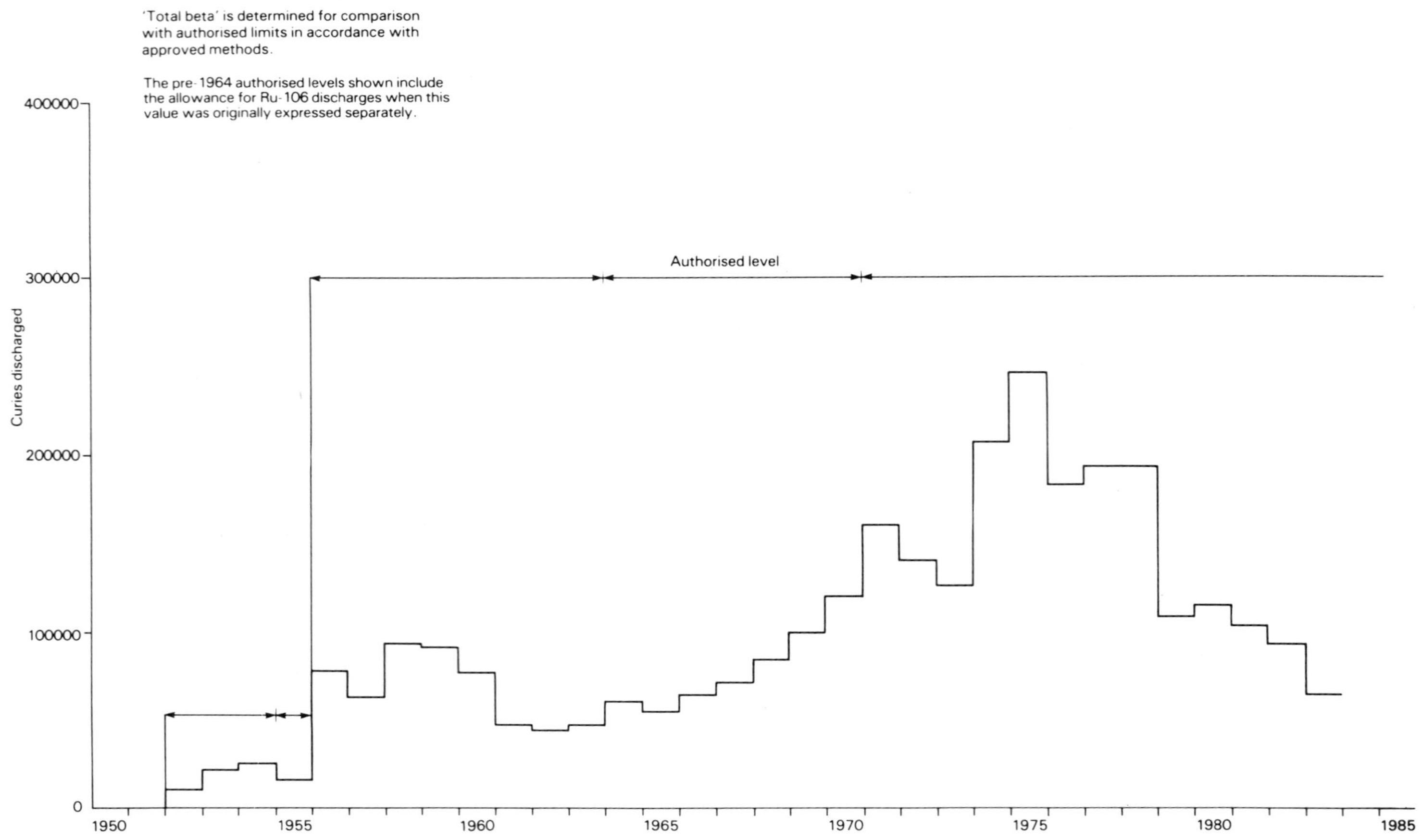

'Total beta' is determined for comparison with authorised limits in accordance with approved methods.
The pre-1964 authorised levels shown include the allowance for Ru-106 discharges when this value was originally expressed separately.
Authorised level
Curies discharged
400000
300000
200000
100000
0
1950
1955
1960
1965
1970
1975
1980
1985

Figure 3.7 Discharges to sea of Caesium-137 from Sellafield site (Figure supplied by BNFL)

1955, 1956 scaled from Sr 90 discharges by NRPB

1952, 1953, assumed to be the same as 1954 discharges by NRPB

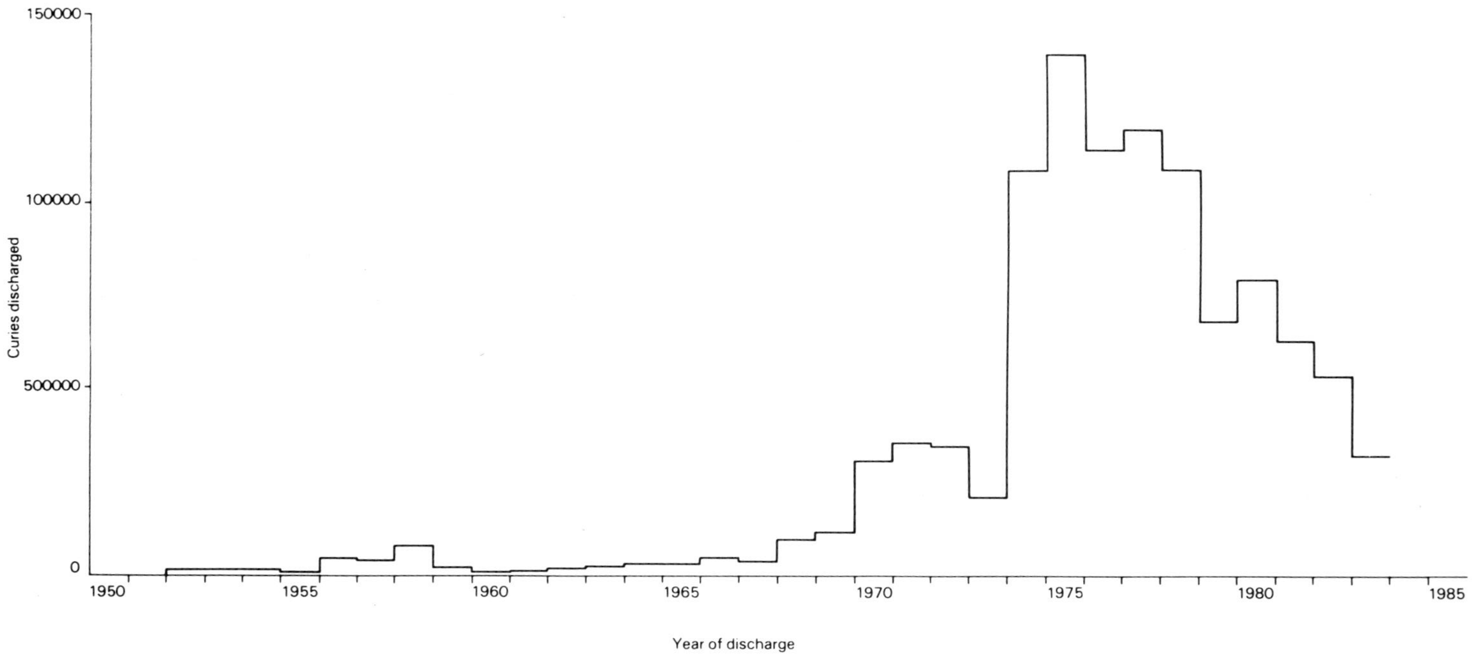

49

Figure 3.8 Discharges to sea of Plutonium-241 from Sellafield site (Figure supplied by BNFL)

Values of Pu-241 prior to 1972 are estimates based on appropriate values of Pu-241:Pu_α depending on fuel reprocessed at that time.

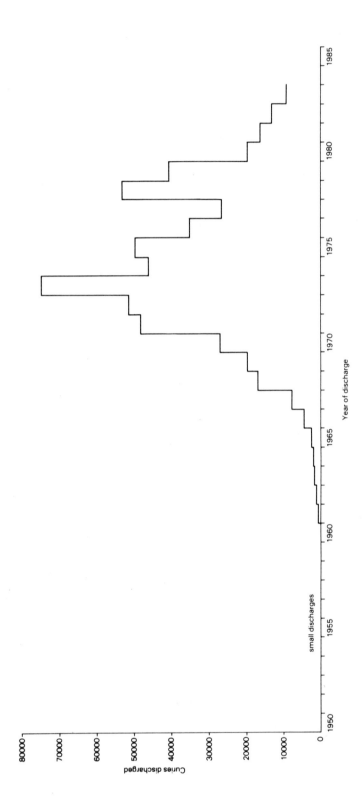

3.29 We understand that airborne discharges are measured but are not at present covered by quantitative limits although the authorisation includes a 'best practicable means' clause designed to provide an ALARA-type restriction.

3.30 'Total alpha', 'total beta' and Iodine-131 discharges to the atmosphere from Sellafield since 1964 are shown in Figures 3.9, 3.10 and 3.11 respectively. The second reprocessing plant came into operation in 1964 (Table 3.1); discharges were not routinely determined as annual figures for earlier years although stack monitoring was used for control purposes. Atmospheric discharges were highest around 1970 with peak figures of 66 Ci for 'total beta' in 1969 and 0·44 curies for 'total alpha' in 1971. Discharge levels have been substantially reduced in subsequent years.

Figure 3.9 Total alpha discharges to atmosphere since 1964 (Figure supplied by BNFL)

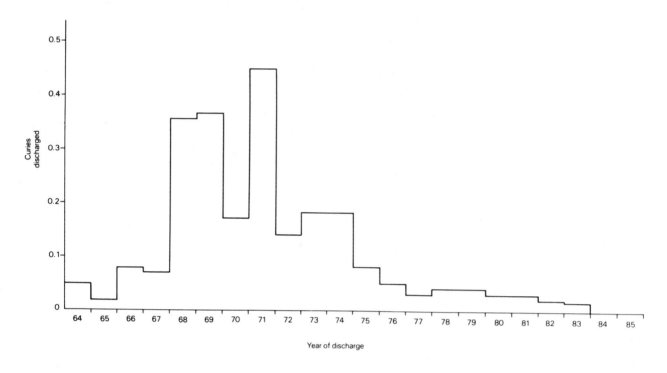

Figure 3.10 Total beta discharges to atmosphere since 1964 (Figure supplied by BNFL)

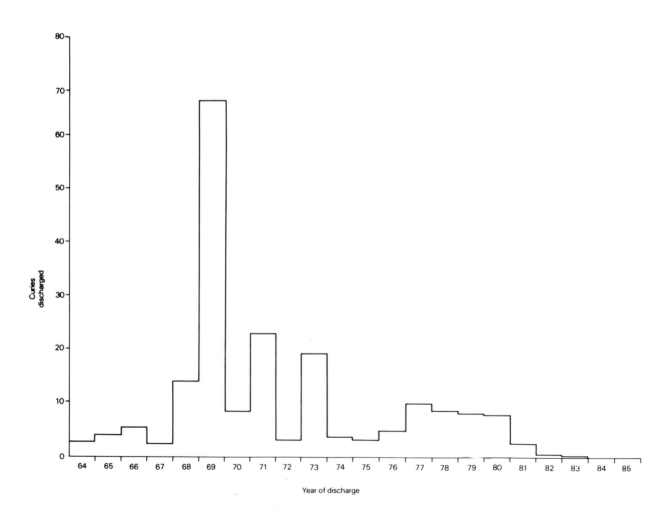

3.31 Discharges are monitored by BNFL and the results are reported to the authorising departments and published in annual reports. The consequential environmental effects are monitored by BNFL subject to the requirements of the Department of the Environment and the Ministry of Agriculture, Fisheries and Food who also carry out their own check monitoring on both the terrestrial and the marine environment. Both Government departments commission relevant research, and MAFF undertake habit surveys and define 'critical groups' for the different aquatic pathways. MAFF also publish an annual report on their marine monitoring results.

3.32 The Department of the Environment and MAFF are expected shortly to issue new authorisations for liquid discharges.

Figure 3.11 Discharges of Iodine-131 to atmosphere since 1964 (Figure supplied by BNFL)

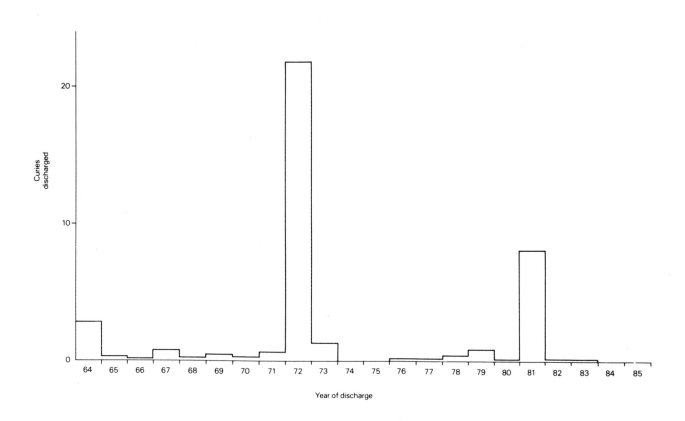

References to Chapter 3

Clough (1983) Further report on the BNFL Radiation Mortality Study. J Soc Radiol Prot *3* (3) 18–20 (SDB 26/12).

Dunster H J (1956) The Discharge of Radioactive Waste Products into the Irish Sea Part 2. Proc Int Conf on Peaceful Uses of Atomic Energy 1955. *9* 712–715 (SDB 626/AP2).

Dunster H J (1958) Disposal of Radioactive Liquid Wastes into Coastal Waters, Proc Int Conf on Peaceful Uses of Atomic Energy, Geneva 1958. *18* 390–399 (SDB 625/AP2).

Fair D R R and MacLean A S. (1956) The Disposal of Waste Products in the Sea. Proc Int Conf on Peaceful Uses of Atomic Energy 1955. Vol *9* 716–717 (SDB 626/AP2).

ICRP Publication 26. Pergamon Press. (SDB 276/EV12).

Royal Commission on Environmental Pollution 6th Report: Nuclear Power and the Environment (1976) HMSO (SDB 161/EV10).

Seligman H. (1956) The Discharge of Radioactive Waste Products into the Irish Sea Part 1. Proc Int Conf on Peaceful Uses of Atomic Energy 1955. *9* 701–711 (SDB 623/AP2).

Wix L F U Fairbairn A and Dunster H J (1960) A review of the monitoring associated with the discharge of radioactive liquid effluent to sea at Windscale from early 1953 until the end of 1958. UKAEA, Harwell.

ANNEX TO CHAPTER 3

SOME OTHER ENVIRONMENTAL FACTORS IN WEST CUMBRIA

INTRODUCTION

A.3.1 Seascale is situated very close to the Sellafield Nuclear Site and its discharges, and radiation is a known cause of leukaemia. This does not necessarily mean that the incidence of leukaemia in the area is related to the discharges from Sellafield. We therefore sought information on other factors possibly relevant to cancer in the West Cumbrian area. We also considered the possibility that the interaction of several causes in the area might be relevant, rather than just one specific cause.

INDUSTRIAL SITES

A.3.2 It was more difficult to collect information on industrial sources of pollution than it had been to collect information on the Sellafield site. Local Factories Inspectorate records do not extend back beyond 10 years, and many of the industries had ceased to trade. We were unable to ascertain what had happened to their records. However in general West Cumbria is not and never has been a highly industrialised area and we found no special features that gave us cause for concern.

A.3.3 The two major industrial sites in the Sellafield area are BNFL, Sellafield and Allbright and Wilson (Marchon Works), Whitehaven. The Allbright and Wilson Chemical Works manufactures chemicals and intermediates. In the past there were several iron and steel works in the area, all of which have now closed, (Table A.3.1); there was also a tar factory at Lowca and several ordnance factories. We have been able to obtain details of present day discharges from only BNFL and Marchon Works.

Table A.3.1 Industry in Area around Sellafield

Type of Industry	Site	Activities	Source of Information	Closed
Iron & Steel	Millom Works	Sinter Plant Blast Furnace Oxygen Steel Process		1970
	Workington Works	Sinter Plant Blast Furnaces Coke Ovens Steel Making		1980
	Distington Engineering Company	Three Cold Blast Cupola		1980
Tar Factory	Lowca (1½ miles north of Whitehaven)		Health and Safety Inspectorate (Local Inspectorate no records)	Probably more than 10 years ago
Ordnance Factories	Sellafield		Ministry of Defence	c. 1945
	Drigg			c. 1945
Ordnance Factories	Distington (Now occupied by High Alloys Extensions Ltd.) Workington Subsequently taken over by British Steel Corporation)		Health and Safety Executive	

Industrial Discharges

A.3.4 *Marchon Works:* Details of liquid and atmospheric discharges were provided by Allbright & Wilson. Solvents used on site are efficiently reclaimed for economic reasons and therefore contribute little to the discharges. Effluent is discharged into Salton Bay at the mean low water mark.

A.3.5 *BNFL:* The major non-radioactive contaminants discharged into the environment are solvents used during nuclear reprocessing, such as tertiary butyl phosphates, odourless kerosene and Butex. Discharges preferentially occur around high tide and the pipe terminates 2·1 km out to sea from the low tide mark.

A.3.6 We found no evidence that these companies released significant quantities of potential chemical carcinogens into the West Cumbrian environment. It is probable that present day discharges into the sea around Sellafield differ substantially from those of 25 years ago. However MAFF told us that the level of pollution in the past is unlikely to have ever been as bad as in industrialised areas such as the Thames and Mersey estuaries.

Human Exposure to Industrial Discharges

A.3.7 The major route for human exposure is thought to be via consumption of seafood caught in the area. This area is not regarded by MAFF Fisheries Division as heavily polluted. MAFF have examined the effects of industrial discharges in the area on seafood, and apart from a small accumulation of cadmium in sediments, levels of pollution in marine organisms and sea water are not significant.

A.3.8 The levels of metals, organochlorines including polychlorinated biphenyls (PCBs) in fish and shellfish caught off the Cumbrian Coast, are similar to or lower than those in fish caught elsewhere around the British Isles, eg plaice caught in the area in 1981 contain up to 0·28 mg/kg mercury while plaice caught in Liverpool Bay area (an area with considerable marine pollution) contain 0·53 mg/kg of mercury; PCB levels in the livers of whiting caught in the Thames estuary are about 16 mg/kg while the level in the livers of plaice caught off the Cumbrian Coast contain 0·26 mg/kg. (MAFF, 1981).

A.3.9 The major effects of airborne pollutants relate to their eventual deposition on the ground and to their effects on plant life. Although it has been suggested that airborne industrial discharges may contribute to respiratory disease, there is no evidence for any connection with the induction of leukaemia.

A.3.10 The above survey is of necessity incomplete and significant discharges into the environment of other toxic chemicals in the past cannot be excluded. However the West Cumbrian coast is not a highly industrialised area, and we were not told of any unusual industrial activities in the past that might be expected to have posed a particular health hazard to the surrounding population.

WATER SUPPLIES*

A.3.11 Seascale's water supply came from Wastwater (which also supplied Ravenglass) between 1950–1975; from 1975 onwards its water supply has come from Ennerdale. Ennerdale, Wastwater and Crummock are lake supplies. Reservoirs are not very important in the area, and storage in service reservoirs is usually only for a few hours and is unlikely to give rise to contamination.

A.3.12 Wastwater is a natural lake whose catchment area contains extensive bracken stands. The catchment area includes Granophyre in Great Gable, and granite on the southern boundary. The rest of the catchment is underlain by Ordovician rocks including the Borrowdale volcanics. Screes and mixed superficial deposits occupy the valley slopes and bottom. Some haematite deposits are present in the upper part of the catchment area.

A.3.13 Ennerdale is also a natural lake with an extensively forested catchment area with some bracken stands on the lake margins. About 30% of the catchment area is underlain by Ennerdale Granophyre (microgranite). The remainder is made up of Skiddaw slates and Borrowdale volcanics. The valley floor above the lake is covered with a mixed suite of superficial deposits of glacial and recent origin. Haematite has been worked on the high ground to the south of the lake where vein-type deposits are found in the Granophyre. Ennerdale also supplies Whitehaven, Egremont, Arlecdon, Lamplugh and Frizington.

Possible Contaminants of Water Supplies

A.3.14 Possible contaminants of water in the context of this investigation are:—

    i. radioactivity—see Chapter 4;

    ii inorganic and organic chemicals such as metals, pesticides, polycyclic aromatic hydrocarbons, nitrate, nitrite and bracken carcinogen;

    iii. bacteria and viruses.

---

* This data was provided largely by the North West Water Authority.

Inorganic and Organic Chemicals

A.3.15 The level of iron in water in the area is high due to the large quantities of iron ore in the area and the many haematite mines. There is no reason to believe this is a health hazard. The North West Water Authority informed us that they did not believe pesticide contamination of water to be significant in the area.

A.3.16 The catchment area supplying West Cumbria contains extensive areas of bracken fern (Pteridium aquilinum). Bracken fern can cause acute toxic symptoms in cattle by a direct radiomimetic effect on the haemopoietic tissues giving rise to haemorrhages, a low white blood cell and low platelet count (Pamekcu et al, 1967). More chronic exposure of cattle to bracken fern causes haematuria, and later benign and sometimes malignant bladder neoplasms (Pamekcu et al 1967, 1968, 1976, 1978). Feeding studies in rats have resulted in lymphopenia, thrombocytopenia and bone marrow suppression. Tumours were induced in the intestines, bladder and mammary glands (Schramm et al, 1970). In mice, leukaemia and pulmonary tumours have been induced (Pamakcu et al, 1972). There is some evidence that the carcinogen may be transmitted via milk (Evans et al, 1982).

A.3.17 Jarrett, (1982) has linked exposure to bracken fern to the induction of squamous cell carcinomas of the upper alimentary tract in cattle in the UK endemically infected with bovine papilloma virus.

A.3.18 Jarrett suggests that bracken fern carcinogen might act as either a promoter, inducer, mutagen or immunosuppressant in animals infected with papilloma virus. He has been able to demonstrate bovine alimentary papilloma virus DNA sequences in these squamous cell carcinomas (Campo et al, 1980, Jarrett et al, 1981).

A.3.19 There is no convincing evidence for human exposure to or toxicity from bracken fern carcinogen. Seascale is only one of many areas in Cumbria whose water comes from bracken-infested hills, and we have seen in the work of Craft and Openshaw, (1984) that the electoral wards adjacent to Seascale do not have an elevated incidence of leukaemia.

BACTERIA AND VIRUSES

A.3.20 Of 19 water samples from Seascale tested in 1982 none contained an unsatisfactory level of coliforms (usually taken as an indicator of faecal contamination). No data were obtained on levels of viruses in water.

Human Viruses and Leukaemia

A.3.21 There is now a substantial body of scientific evidence concerning viruses that cause tumours in animals, and related human viruses have been implicated as aetiological agents in the induction of human cancer (Weiss, 1984a). In all cases virus infection alone appears insufficient for tumour induction and other contributory causes or co-factors such as malaria (in induction of Burkitt's lymphoma by Epstein-Barr virus), alcohol or aflatoxin (in the development of hepatocellular carcinoma following hepatitis B infection) and sunlight or inherited disorders (in the development of skin cancer from papilloma virus infection) are also necessary. New strains of human papilloma viruses (HPV-16, HPV-18) are strongly implicated in cervical cancer (Gissmann, 1984). So far there is no evidence to suggest that animal tumour viruses can cause tumours in humans.

A.3.22 Human adult T-cell leukaemia virus (HTLV-1 or ATLV) is the only human virus that has been implicated in human leukaemia to date. This is a retrovirus which induces an aggressive variant of mature T-cell leukaemia. HTLV-1 has so far been identified as occurring mainly in South West Japan, in the Caribbean basin, in Central America, and in Africa (Gallo, 1984). A related virus, HTLV-2, has been isolated from one adult patient with hairy cell leukaemia. The natural mode of transmission of these agents has not yet been established. More recently a new virus, LAV or HTLV-3, has been identified as the probable cause of Acquired Immune Deficiency Syndrome (AIDS) (Weiss, 1984b). HTLV-1 and HTLV-2 have not been detected in any cases of childhood leukaemia, but the AIDS retrovirus does affect infants of infected mothers.

A.3.23 Until 4 years ago, no human oncogenic retroviruses were known. In the last 4 years 3 such viruses have been discovered; there may well be more remaining to be discovered and there is no reason to believe any such viruses would exclusively affect adults.

A.3.24 Several authors have reported that *in utero* exposure of the foetus to virus infections contracted by the mother may be followed by cancer in the children. In 1958, Stewart et al reported an association between viral infections of pregnant women and the development of cancer in children born of the pregnancies. In 1972, Fredrick and Alberman reported that a follow-up study of maternal illness in pregnancy had demonstrated a large excess of leukaemia in infants whose mothers had reported an attack of influenza during pregnancy. The study was based on 16,750 infants born in one week in March 1958, who had survived the neonatal period. The mothers of 12% reported having influenza during the 1957–58 pandemic; 8 of these developed cancer, a five-fold increase when compared to the other children; 6 were diagnosed as suffering from leukaemia. Subsequently there have been a number of studies producing conflicting results (Hakulinen et al, (1973); Randolph and Heath, (1974); Mackenzie and Houghton, (1974); Curnew and Varma, (1974); Austin et al, (1975). Similar reports of cancer, especially leukaemia, following varicella infection in the mothers during the relevant pregnancy have been published (Adelstein and Donovan 1972).

A.3.25 In summary, therefore, there is no known human leukaemia virus that could be postulated as contributing to the observed excess leukaemia incidence in young people near Sellafield. Research in this area is very active at present, and further developments will no doubt occur rapidly. The available evidence would suggest that any virus that played a part in leukaemia induction would do so in a multifactorial manner, rather than acting in isolation; the tumour viruses so far described generally being widespread in any population and only causing malignancy as a late and rare consequence of infection, following some other additional environmental agent. Any possible transplacental effect of virus infection during pregnancy is unlikely to give rise to more than a doubling in the overall cancer incidence in childhood.

COMBINED EFFECTS

A.3.26 The joint effects of chemical, physical and biological agents are of potentially great importance, but good quality scientific data on such effects are not readily available. UNSCEAR (1982) examined the evidence for combined action of ionising radiation and carcinogens, but found available data incomplete and evidence for a promotor effect conflicting. There is some evidence that tobacco smoke results in shortening of time to the appearance of lung cancer induced by the alpha particles of radon daughters.

The mode of action of this observed effect is as yet unclear. Evidence for synergism between radiation and viruses, bacteria, or diet is either equivocal or negative (UNSCEAR 1982) but the possibility cannot be excluded either in the context of the Sellafield discharges, or in the general context. However, the difference between the radiation dose calculated as being received by those living in the area around the Sellafield site and the dose received by the same people from background radiation is probably not sufficient to make a synergistic effect likely at Seascale or in Millom Rural District (see Chapter 4).

CONCLUSION

A.3.27 While it is possible to postulate agents that might act synergistically with radiation, we have found no convincing evidence for any unexpected environmental carcinogen or agent peculiar to the area around Sellafield.

References

Adelstein A M and Donovan J W (1972) Br Med J *4* 629

Austin D F, Karp S and Dworsky R et al. (1975) Excess leukaemia in cohorts of children born following influenza epidemics. Am J Epidemiol. *101*, 77–83.

Campo M S Moar M H Jarrett W F H and Laird H M (1980) Nature *286* 180–182.

Craft A W and Openshaw. Childhood Cancer in the Northern Region 1968–82: A Preliminary Report to the Black Advisory Group (SDB 555/H21).

Curnew M G M Varma A O A and Christine B W et al. (1974) Childhood leukaemia and maternal infectious diseases during pregnancy. JNCI *53* 943–947.

Essex M et al (1983) Science *220* 859–62.

Evans I A Porok J H Cole R C et al (1982) Proc Roy Soc Edinburgh *81B* 65–77.

Fredrick J and Alberman E D (1972) Brit. Med. J. *2* 485–488.

Gallo R C (1984) Human T-cell leukaemia-lymphoma virus and T-cell malignancies. Cancer Surveys *3* 113–159.

Gissman L (1984) Papilloma viruses and their association with cancer in animals and in man Cancer Surveys *3* 161–181.

Hakulinen T Hovi L and Karkinen-Jaaskelainen M et al (1973) Association between influenza during pregnancy and childhood leukaemia. Brit. Med. J. *4*, 265–267.

Jarrett W F H (1981) Papilloma viruses and cancer *in* Recent Advances in Histopathology *11* 35–48.

Jarrett W F H (1982) Proc Roy Soc Edin *81B* 79–83.

Mackenzie J S and Houghton M (1974) Influenza infections during pregnancy: Association with congenital malformations and with subsequent neoplasms in children and potential hazards of virus vaccines. Bact Rev *38* 356–370.

MAFF: Aquatic Environment Monitoring Report (1981).

Pamecku A M Gokocy S K and Price J M (1967) Cancer Res *27* 917–924.

Pamecku J M and Pamecku A M (1968) Cancer Research *28* 2247–2251.

Pamecku A M Erturk E Price J M and Bryon G T (1972). Cancer Research *32* 1442–1445.

Pamecku A M Price J M and Bryon G T (1976) Vet Pathol *13* 110–122.

Pamecku A M Erturk E Yalciner S, Milli U and Bryon G T, (1978) Cancer Research *38* 1556–1560.

Randolph V L and Heath C W Jr. (1974) Influenza during pregnancy in relation to subsequent childhood leukaemia and lymphoma. Am. J. Epidemiol. *100*, 399–409.

Schramm P Philip R B and Gowdey C W (1970) Am J Vet Res *31* 191–197.

UNSCEAR (1982) United Nations Scientific Committee on the Effects of Atomic Radiation. New York.

Weiss R A (1984a) Viruses and Human Cancer *in* The Microbe 1984: Part I Viruses, ed. B W J Mahy and J R Pattison Soc for Gen Microbiology Symposium *36*. Cambridge University Press.

Weiss R A (1984b) Retro-Viruses linked with AIDS Nature *309* 12–13.

CHAPTER 4

RADIATION EXPOSURE OF YOUNG PEOPLE IN SEASCALE AND RECOMMENDATIONS

SUMMARY

4.1 The sources of radiation to which the general public around Sellafield are exposed are considered in turn, and the dose to the red bone marrow from each source is calculated for the under 20-year old population of Seascale. (It is irradiation of the red bone marrow that is responsible for radiation-induced leukaemia.) The contributions to this dose from low <u>Linear Energy Transfer</u> (LET) radiation (ie beta and gamma rays) and high LET radiation (ie alpha rays) are also calculated separately. (See Annex to this Chapter for a discussion of the biological significance of these different types of radiation.) Only the course of our argument is given here, the evidence upon which it is based is contained in this Chapter and in the three NRPB documents to be published at the same time as this Report (NRPB R170; R171; R172; 1984). The units for measuring radiation and its effects are defined in the Table at the end of the Glossary and are explained in the Glossary.

4.2 Table 4.3 summarises the calculated doses to the red bone marrow of the estimated 175 children born in Seascale in the five years from 1950 and resident there until 1970 (the 1950 cohort), from natural background, medical radiation and nuclear fallout. The total dose equivalent to the red bone marrow from low LET radiation is 26 mSv, while that from high LET radiation is 0·98 mSv. The total red bone marrow dose equivalent is therefore about 27 mSv. This figure is about average for radiation exposure from these sources in the United Kingdom.

4.3 Radiation is a known cause of leukaemia. Since we are all exposed to background radiation, it has been postulated that this radiation causes at least some of the leukaemias occurring in the UK. We do not know what proportion of the leukaemias are caused by background radiation, but it cannot be more than all of them. If it is assumed that all deaths from leukaemia in the UK are caused by background radiation then we can calculate that the 27 mSv exposure experienced by the 175 individuals in the 1950 cohort from all background sources excluding discharges from Sellafield whether accidental or planned, would be expected to have given rise to 0·1 deaths from leukaemia in the 20 years from 1950, based on the death rate from leukaemia in young people in England and Wales (paragraph 4.45).

4.4 The Seascale young people are exposed to additional radiation due to the discharges of radioactivity from Sellafield. The red bone marrow dose equivalent from the Sellafield site discharges for an individual in the 1950 cohort from 1950–1970 has been calculated as being 3·5 mSv, which is 13% of the dose equivalent calculated above as occurring from background radiation. This includes a dose equivalent of 0·8 mSv from the Windscale fire in 1957, (3% of the dose equivalent from background radiation) (paragraph 4.46).

4.5 Assuming a linear relationship between dose received and risk of death from leukaemia, this means that the dose received by the 1950 cohort from the Sellafield discharges would be expected to give rise to a maximum of 13% of 0·1 additional deaths from leukaemia, ie 0·013 cases. In their report, NRPB consider seven similar 5 year cohorts between 1945 and 1975 in Seascale. For these seven cohorts the expected risk of death from leukaemia from the discharges will be less than $0·013 \times 7 = 0·091$ additional deaths (paragraph 4.47). In fact we are aware of 4 deaths from leukaemia before the age of 20 years in Seascale since 1945 (cases 1, 3, 5 and 6, Table 2.1), while 0·5 deaths would be expected in the same population using OPCS figures for England and Wales. Therefore there are 3·5 additional deaths from leukaemia in Seascale. This is approximately 40 times more than can be calculated as likely to arise from exposure of the population to the radioactive discharges from the Sellafield site (paragraph 4.48).

4.6 In calculating the expected number of deaths from leukaemia in this way we are using actually observed levels of background, ie low dose-rate, radiation to give us the maximum possible risk factor, unless there is, in Seascale, an unusual concentration of highly susceptible children. We are, however, making the following assumptions:

a. that conclusions on quantities of food consumed derived from habit surveys and other sources are reasonably accurate (paragraph 4.59);

b. that the gut transfer factors for the actinides and other isotopes such as Ruthenium, which are believed to cross the gut wall poorly, are reasonably accurate (paragraph 4.60 et seq);

c. that the model used to calculate the dose to the red bone marrow is reasonably accurate (paragraph 4.76);

d. and that the contribution to exposure from unknown sources or from undetected accidents does not add up to 40 times the total dose calculated to be received by the population from the known discharges over the last 30 years.

4.7 With these qualifications the Sellafield discharges, including those from the Windscale fire and known accidents, are predicted to have resulted in less than 0.1 additional deaths from leukaemia in Seascale between 1945–1980 in the under 20 year old population.

4.8 There have been approximately 1,220 children born in Seascale since 1950. 0·1 additional deaths from leukaemia in 1,200 children would represent a risk of 1 in 12,000 over a period in excess of 20 years or approximately a 1 in 240,000 risk per annum, ie a chance of about 4 in a million of dying from leukaemia before the age of 20 years from living in Seascale each year for under 20 year olds.

INTRODUCTION

4.9 The sources of radiation to which the general population of West Cumbria are exposed are:

a. natural background

b. medical diagnostic and medical therapeutic procedures

c. fall-out from atmospheric testing of nuclear weapons

d. miscellaneous other sources

e. radioactive releases both to sea and to atmosphere from routine operations at nuclear sites in the country and as a consequence of accidents and incidents.

4.10 Those working at Sellafield or any other establishment where radioactive substances or ionising radiations are in the environment, or are used, may also be exposed as a consequence of their work.

4.11 There is no evidence that exposure from the first 4 causes is likely to be different in West Cumbria from in the rest of the United Kingdom, although there will be regional variations. However, because West Cumbria contains the Sellafield site, radiation exposure from the fifth source will differ from that in other parts of the United Kingdom.

4.12 Adults and children have rather different habits and consequently may have different exposures to radiation; much of the information generally available does not pay particular attention to childhood exposure. Since we are particularly interested in exposure in the under 25 age group, we asked NRPB to prepare a comprehensive review of radiation exposure in young people resident in Seascale, including *in utero* exposure, using the best available data and including exposure due to known accidents and to the Windscale fire in 1957. NRPB also critically reassessed possible routes of exposure as part of this study (NRPB R171, 1984). A diagram of their assessment procedure is shown in Figure 4.1.

Figure 4.1 Schematic diagram of assessment procedure

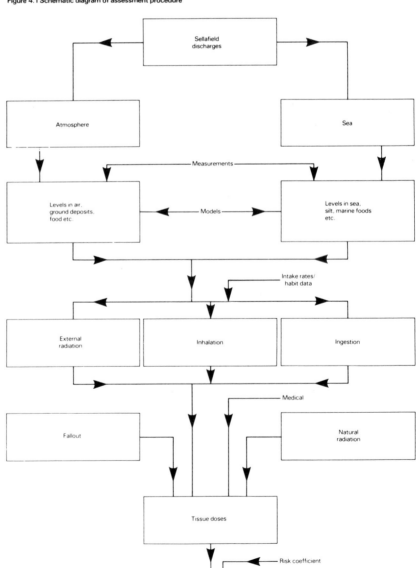

4.13 In this Chapter we shall consider the contribution to radiation dose from the 5 sources outlined above. We consider the low <u>linear energy transfer</u> (LET) (beta and gamma rays) and the high LET (alpha rays) component separately in each case, since the biological effect per unit absorbed dose differs for these 2 types of radiation by a variable factor depending on the rate at which the dose is received (see Annex to this Chapter). We consider the red bone marrow dose in particular, because this is the target organ for induction of leukaemia by radiation. Except where otherwise stated, doses given in this Chapter are quoted from the NRPB review (NRPB R171, 1984).

a. Background Radiation

4.14 Natural radiation pervades the whole environment, and it is helpful to consider the likely significance of any additional radiation exposure in this context. Radiation reaches the earth from outer space; the earth itself contains radioactive elements; and natural radioactivity is present in the food we eat and in some of the elements contained in our body.

4.15 <u>Cosmic rays</u> penetrate the atmosphere from space. The total dose from cosmic rays to all tissues of the body can be assessed as 300 μGy in a year at Seascale and this is almost all low LET radiation.

4.16 Terrestrial <u>radionuclides</u> include Potassium-40 and the radionuclides in the Uranium-238 and Thorium-232 series. All materials in the earth's crust contain these radionuclides and the population is continuously exposed externally to gamma radiation resulting from their decay, and internally to alpha, beta and gamma radiation from inhalation and ingestion routes.

4.17 Measurements of outdoor gamma ray dose rates have been made in West Cumbria. A mean of 42nGy per hour was obtained, which is only marginally above the national average. Gamma ray doses in dwellings in Seascale are not available, but 6 dwellings in the Cumbrian area have been monitored by NRPB and gave results very near to the national average of about 65 nGy per hour. Assuming average usage of indoors and outdoors, the average dose to Seascale residents can be assessed as 400 μGy per year from gamma rays from external terrestrial radionuclides.

4.18 <u>Radon decay products</u> in the atmosphere originate from the decay of <u>Thorium-232 and Uranium-238</u>. Radon is a gas and so can move through rocks, soils or building materials in which it is generated and be released from the surface. Out of doors, radon is soon dispersed in the atmosphere but indoors it can accumulate due to limited ventilation. Indoor concentrations vary widely depending on the ground the house stands on, the material the house is constructed of, and the degree of ventilation.

4.19 Radiation from radon decay products is predominantly high LET radiation and the dose is delivered almost entirely to the lung tissue. NRPB estimated that a dose of 420 μGy is received per year from this source.

4.20 Potassium-40 is the major source of internal low LET irradiation. This radionuclide is always present in natural Potassium. The average annual dose has been estimated as 270 μGy per year to red bone marrow. The other main contributors of dose from internal irradiation are Lead-210, Polonium-210 and Radium-226. These give about 2·3 μGy of high LET radiation to the red bone marrow per year (NRPB R171, 1984; Table 8.5.c).

	4.21 In their report, NRPB calculate the doses of high and low LET radiation from natural backgound to red bone marrow for individuals in 7 cohorts

Dose to red bone marrow
from natural background
radiation in 20 years
for Seascale young people

4.21 In their report, NRPB calculate the doses of high and low LET radiation from natural backgound to red bone marrow for individuals in 7 cohorts of children born in Seascale at 5 yearly intervals from 1945–1975 and assumed to be living in Seascale since birth. An estimate of the *in utero* contribution is also included. Table 4.1 shows that the total dose to red bone marrow from natural background for the 1950 cohort up to 1970 is 47·5 μGy of high LET radiation and 20,000 μGy of low LET radiation. High LET radiation therefore contributes 0·2% of the total absorbed dose to red bone marrow from natural background.

Table 4.1 Radiation dose to red bone marrow from natural background from 1950–1970 for an individual in a cohort of those born in Seascale in 1950 and resident in Seascale until 1970.

Radionuclide [+]	High LET dose (μGy)	High LET dose equivalent (μSv*)	Low LET dose (μGy)	Low LET dose equivalent (μSv*)
Pb–210	29	580	18	18
Po–210	5·5	110	$4·4 \times 10^{-6}$	$4·4 \times 10^{-6}$
Ra–226	13	260	2·2	2·2
Gamma Emitters	—	—	$2·0 \times 10^{4}$	$2·0 \times 10^{4}$
Total	47·5 (0·2% of total)	950 (5% of total)	$2·0 \times 10^{4}$ (99·8% of total)	$2·0 \times 10^{4}$ (95% of total)

*Quality Factor=20 for high LET radiation
Quality Factor=1 for low LET radiation
For explanation of high and low LET radiation see Annex to Chapter 4) (page 84).
[+] See Table 4.11 for key for abbreviations for radionuclides (page 83)
Total dose to red bone marrow=$2·1 \times 10^{4}$ μSv (21 mSv)

(From NRPB R 171, 1984; Table 8.5c)

b. Medical Irradiation

4.22 Medical irradiation includes doses from diagnostic X-rays and radioisotopes and radiotherapy with X- or gamma rays. For the average individual the largest artificial exposure is derived from these sources, and within this, diagnostic X-ray examinations are responsible for the major part of medical exposure. A large proportion of the population are not exposed to radiation from this source each year, and certain individuals may receive several times the average dose from this source. In a Swedish study an X-ray of lungs and heart was reported to give an average whole body dose of 0·57 mGy (57 mrad), a bone marrow dose of 0·54 mGy (54 mrad), and a thyroid dose of 0·24 mGy (24 mrad). A retrograde pyelogram (involving screening over a period of time rather than a single exposure) is estimated as giving 10 mGy (1,000 mrad) whole body dose (UNSCEAR, 1978) which is twice the ICRP recommended limit for annual exposure to the public from sources other than background and medical sources. These doses are justifiable because the potential benefit of reaching a correct diagnosis greatly outweighs the risk from the radiation exposure.

4.23 There are no data available on frequency of radiological examinations in West Cumbria, but equally there are no reasons to suppose an unusual pattern in the area, and the 1977 survey of diagnostic radiology practices in Great Britain found the number of X-ray examinations per head of population in the Nothern Regional Health Authority to be within 10 per cent of that for Britain as a whole.

4.24 Annual mean red bone marrow doses from diagnostic radiology practices in the UK were estimated in 1957/8 by a Committee under the chairmanship of Lord Adrian (1966) and a new study is currently underway. The NRPB report calculated the average radiation dose up to 1970 from medical exposure for individuals born in 1950 as $3 \cdot 9 \times 10^3$ μGy. This will all be from low LET radiation and includes a component for foetal exposure (NRPB R171, 1984; Table 8.4).

c. Nuclear weapon fallout

4.25 This has contributed to background exposure since the late 1940's. The periods of most intensive atmospheric testing were 1955–58 and 1961–62. The main constituents of nuclear fallout are fission products such as Strontium-90, Caesium-137, Cerium-144, Strontium-89, Ruthenium-106, Zirconium-95 and Iodine-131. Those components of fallout which are particulate tend to deposit in any region in proportion to the rainfall in the area.

4.26 The external gamma dose from ground deposited material from fallout is mainly due to Caesium-137 and Zirconium-95. The annual absorbed dose rate in air at 1 metre above ground has been measured at Chilton in Oxfordshire since 1951. The average annual rainfall in the Sellafield area is about twice that at Chilton and the dose rates from this source can be estimated from the Chilton figures by scaling for this factor. Allowance also has to be made for shielding by buildings and for time spent indoors. NRPB calculate a total dose of 420 μGy red bone marrow from this source for a 20 year old living since birth in 1950 in Seascale (NRPB R171, 1984; Table 8.3c).

4.27 The concentrations of radionuclides in milk and other foodstuffs in the UK have been measured by the Agricultural Research Council Laboratories at Wantage, Oxfordshire since 1958, and by NRPB since 1978. The concentrations of the more important radionuclides in air and rain have been measured since 1954 by the Atomic Energy Research Establishment (AERE) at Harwell, and since 1975 by NRPB.

4.28 Strontium-90 tends to become fixed in soil and very little reaches drinking water supplies. The main dietary sources are dairy produce, flour and cereals. Milk can be used as an indicator of total dietary intake of Strontium-90.

4.29 The major exposure pathway for Caesium-137 is through diet, and milk is a good indicator of dietary levels. Caesium-137 levels in milk have been measured since 1961.

4.30 Iodine-131 has a half-life of only 8 days and therefore only its concentration in milk is important. It has been assayed in milk since 1961, but levels have been below the limit of detection except for in 1961–62 and 1976–77.

4.31 Plutonium-239, -240, and -238 in fallout have been measured by AERE, Harwell since 1961 and NRPB since 1975. There appears to be little variation with rainfall.

Summary of contribution of Fallout to Background Radiation

4.32 Table 4.2 summarises the red bone marrow dose calculated by NRPB for a 20 year-old resident in Seascale born in 1950 using best available estimates. 1.7 μGy of high LET and 2,200 μGy of low LET radiation is received by an individual by the age of 20 from fallout.

Table 4.2 Radiation dose to red bone marrow from nuclear fallout from 1950–1970 for an individual in a cohort of those born in Seascale in 1950 and resident in Seascale until 1970.

Radionuclide[+]	High LET dose (μGy)	High LET dose equivalent (μSv*)	Low LET dose (μGy)	Low LET dose equivalent (μSv*)
Sr-90			7.3×10^2	7.3×10^2
Ru-106			1.9	1.9
Cs-137			6.7×10^2	6.7×10^2
Ce-144			34	34
Pu-238	1.7×10^{-1}	3.4	3.5×10^{-4}	3.5×10^{-4}
Pu-239	1.6	32	2.2×10^{-3}	2.2×10^{-3}
I-131			1.7×10^{-1}	1.7×10^{-1}
Sr-89			2.4×10^2	2.4×10^2
C-14			71	71
H-3			6.7	6.7
External			4.2×10^2	4.2×10^2
Total	1.7 (0.1% of total)	35.4 (2% of total)	2.2×10^3 (99.9% of total)	2.2×10^3 (98% of total)

Total Dose to red bone marrow = 2.2×10^3 μSv = 2.2 mSv

*Quality Factor for High LET radiation = 20
 Quality Factor for Low LET radiation = 1
 For definition of High and Low LET radiation see Annex to Chapter 4
[+] See Table 4.11 for key to abbreviations for radionuclides (page 83)

(from NRPB R171, 1984; Table 8.3c)

d. Miscellaneous other sources

4.33 These include such things as the luminous dials of watches painted with radium. Their contribution to red bone marrow doses is insignificant.

SUMMARY OF RADIATION EXPOSURE EXCLUDING THAT FROM SELLAFIELD DISCHARGES

4.34 Radiation exposure of the population in Seascale and adjacent areas from sources apart from nuclear site discharges is likely to be similar to that in the rest of the country. Although there are deficiencies in the data for this part of the country, none of the available evidence suggests that the population is exposed to unusually high levels of radiation from the above sources.

4.35 The total red bone marrow dose to individuals in the 1950 cohort living in Seascale from the above sources is estimated by NRPB to be 48.7 μGy from high LET radiation and 26,100 μGy from low LET radiation (Table 4.3). Therefore 99.8% of the absorbed dose to red bone marrow from the above sources derives from low LET radiation and 0.2% from high LET radiation.

Table 4.3 Radiation dose to red bone marrow from all background sources from 1950–1970 for an individual in a cohort of those born in Seascale in 1950 and resident in Seascale until 1970.

Source	High LET dose (μGy)	High LET dose equivalent (μSv*)	Low LET dose (μGy)	Low LET dose equivalent (μSv*)
Natural Background	47	950	20×10^3	20×10^3
Nuclear Fallout	1.7	35.4	2.2×10^3	2.2×10^3
Medical Radiation	—	—	3.9×10^3	3.9×10^3
Total	48.7 (0.2% of total)	985.4 (4% of total)	26.1×10^3 (99.8% of total)	26.1×10^3 (96.0% of total)

Total radiation from background sources = 27.085×10^3 μSv
= 27 mSv

*Quality Factor = 20 for High LET radiation
 Quality Factor = 1 for Low LET radiation
 (See Annex to Chapter 4 for explanation of high and low LET radiation)

Risk estimates from population exposure to radiation

4.36 The main late somatic effect of radiation in man is cancer. Usually no clinical distinction can be made between cancers induced by radiation and those occuring from other causes. There are considerable uncertainties regarding the radiation doses to human populations in which excess leukaemia rates have been observed subsequent to radiation exposure.

Risk of leukaemia following radiation of the parent prior to conception

4.37 The incidence of leukaemia in children of Japanese survivors conceived after the atom bombs were dropped has not demonstrated an excess risk of leukaemia (see NRPB R171, 1984; Tables 7.4 and 7.5), whether one or both parents were exposed in either city. These data would suggest that the risk of leukaemia arising in children from gonadal irradiation of the parents is small.

4.38 At present there is no convincing evidence that establishes such a mechanism for cancer induction in man although only limited data is available.

Risks of leukaemia following irradiation in utero

4.39 Risk estimates by UNSCEAR are based on data from Stewart and Kneale (1970a, 1970b) and others, (NRPB R171, 1984; Chapter 7 paragraphs 7.2.3 and 7.3.7). The UNSCEAR estimate is $2 \cdot 3 \times 10^{-3}$ cancer deaths induced/year/gray of radiation exposure, for doses to the foetus in the range of $0 \cdot 002 - 0 \cdot 2$ Gy; the cancers occurring over a 10 year period. Leukaemias would be expected to contribute about half of the cases. Monson and MacMahon (1984) in their study of children in the United States receiving pre-natal diagnostic X-rays, demonstrated an excess incidence of cancers in the 0–5 years from birth; a declining incidence of excess cancers from 6–9 years from birth and no excess of cancers after 9 years. The total risk of developing a fatal induced malignancy from *in utero* exposure to low LET radiation may therefore be in the region of $2 \cdot 0 - 2 \cdot 5 \times 10^{-2}$/Gy of exposure to the foetus with a risk of death from developing leukaemia of $1 \cdot 0 - 1 \cdot 25 \times 10^{-2}$/Gy of exposure to the foetus. For their report NRPB assumed a total risk of death from leukaemia of $1 \cdot 25 \times 10^{-2}$/Gy from *in utero* irradiation, which is at the upper end of the range of values recommended by UNSCEAR (1972), and assumed that the deaths would be expressed within 9 years of birth with no latent period: 36% would appear in the first 3 years, 40% in the next 3 years and the remainder in the last 3 years. These figures apply to low LET radiation. NRPB used a relative biological effectiveness (RBE) factor of 20 to calculate risks from high LET radiation, (See Annex to this Chapter).

Risk of leukaemia in children up to age 10 years

4.40 Beebe et al (1978) reported that the incidence of leukaemia in the survivors under age 10 at the time the bombs were dropped on Hiroshima and Nagasaki was about 50% greater than that in the rest of the exposed population. The Hiroshima and Nagasaki data were not collected until 5 years after the bombs were dropped, and therefore cases dying during these first 5 years may not be included in the study. In their calculations NRPB have assumed that the period of risk is 15 years with half the cases occurring in the first five years.

Leukaemia in young persons and adults

4.41 Based on data from ankylosing spondylitis patients (Smith and Doll, 1982) and the incomplete Hiroshima and Nagasaki data (Beebe et al, 1978) NPRB assumed that the total risk of leukaemia induced by exposure to low LET radiation is $3 \cdot 5 \times 10^{-3}$/Gy with 50% of cases appearing in the first 7 years, with no latent period, 33% in the next 7 years and the remainder in a final 7 year period.

4.42 The only evidence covering the entire potential induction period on leukaemia induction by high LET radiation alone is from Thorotrast used as a contrast medium in diagnostic radiology in the past. Data on the induction of lung and bone cancer in animals and on bone cancer in man suggest that an RBE of 20 is reasonable for doses of about 0·1 Gy (low LET) upwards. The probable increase in the RBE for high LET radiation at low doses and low dose rates is likely to arise not because the risks of high LET radiation are greater, but because the risks of low LET radiation, whatever their value, are smaller (see Annex to this Chapter).

4.43 In summary, for calculating the risks from natural background radiation, medical radiation and Sellafield discharges, NRPB used a risk factor for deaths from leukaemia by radiation of $1·25 \times 10^{-2}$/Gy for irradiation *in utero*; 5×10^{-3}/Gy at ages 0–9 years, and $3·5 \times 10^{-3}$/Gy for ages 10 years and over for low LET exposure (Table 4.4). They used a relative biological effectiveness factor of 20 for calculating effects from high LET radiation.

Table 4.4   Risk estimates* for radiation-induced leukaemia

Age (in years)	Risk Estimate* (Low LET radiation)	Source
In Utero	$1·25 \times 10^{-2}$/gray	Upper limit of UNSCEAR
0–10	$5 \quad \times 10^{-3}$/gray	NRPB
10+	$3·5 \times 10^{-3}$/gray	NRPB
in utero + 0–20	$2·28 \times 10^{-2}$/gray	Comparison with background

*Number of radiation-induced leukaemias expected per gray of radiation exposure

Risk Factor Limits

4.44 All of the above estimates can be criticised on the grounds that they are based on acute exposure rather than chronic exposure to radiation, and on dose values concerning which there is at least some uncertainty. The upper limit for the risk factor for death from leukaemia in those up to the age of 20 can be found if one postulates that all deaths from childhood leukaemia in England and Wales up to the age of 20 years are caused by the red bone marrow dose from background radiation either *in utero* or post-natally. This is an unlikely "worst-case" postulate, Stewart and Kneale calculated that 70% of childhood cancer was the greatest proportion likely to be due to natural background, extrapolating from their work on diagnostic X-ray exposure *in utero*, (Stewart and Kneale, 1983). The advantage of this method is that the upper limit risk factor thus obtained will apply to doses and dose rates that are of similar size to the doses received from background radiation and of similar size to the doses calculated as received from the discharges from the Sellafield site.

4.45 NRPB have calculated the mortality from leukaemia expected to occur during the first 20 years, in any cohort of 175 children born in England and Wales in 1950–55 and therefore comparable to the Seascale '1950 cohort'. Approximately 0·1 cases of leukaemia would be expected (NRPB R171, 1984; Table A1). 0·5 cases would be expected from 7 cohorts (1,225 children) starting in 1945 in five year periods and calculating the risk until the age of 20 or until 1980, whichever occurs first, again to form a group comparable to the 7 Seascale cohorts. Using the postulate that all childhood leukaemias in England and Wales are caused by background radiation and the estimate of the dose received from all background radiation in Table 4.3 an estimate of a risk factor of approximately 2×10^{-2}/Gy for the induction of leukaemia by radiation can be obtained. This is about 4–6 times the risk estimate NRPB used for exposure to radiation in childhood, and slightly less than twice the risk estimate NRPB used for exposure *in utero* (Table 4.4), in their review (NRPB R171, 1984; Chapter 7). It is therefore about 5 times more conservative over the 20 year period than the NRPB risk estimate of leukaemia deaths from radiation.

4.46 Seascale young people are exposed to additional radiation due to the discharges of radioactivity from the Sellafield site, both planned and accidental. The NRPB have reassessed the doses received by the young people of Seascale from these sources in Chapters 4 and 8 of their report, (NRPB R171, 1984). The doses to the red bone marrow from routine and accidental Sellafield discharges are shown in Table 4.5 and the doses to red bone marrow from the Windscale fire in Table 4.6, the way that these dose estimates are obtained is explained in detail in paragraphs 4.49–4.62. The red bone marrow dose from the Sellafield discharges for individuals in the 1950–1970 cohort is calculated to be $3 \cdot 7 \mu$Gy high LET and $2,600 \mu$Gy low LET radiation, while that from the Windscale fire is $13 \cdot 9 \mu$Gy high LET and 560μGy low LET radiation. The total dose equivalent (allowing for the differing biological effectiveness of the two types of radiation) to the red bone marrow from Sellafield activities (Tables 4.5 and 4.6) is therefore $2 \cdot 7 + 0 \cdot 8 = 3 \cdot 5$ mSv. This is 13% of the dose equivalent from background sources.

Table 4.5 Radiation dose to red bone marrow from Sellafield discharges and accidental releases (excluding Windscale fire) from 1950–1970 for an individual in a cohort of those born in Seascale in 1950 and resident in Seascale until 1970.

Radionuclide[+]	High LET dose (μGy)	High LET dose equivalent (μSv*)	Low LET dose (μGy)	Low LET dose equivalent (μSv*)
Sr- 90			$3 \cdot 2 \times 10^2$	$3 \cdot 2 \times 10^2$
Zr- 95			$1 \cdot 9$	$1 \cdot 9$
Nb- 95			$4 \cdot 9 \times 10^1$	$4 \cdot 9 \times 10^1$
Ru-106			$1 \cdot 4 \times 10^2$	$1 \cdot 4 \times 10^2$
Cs-134			$1 \cdot 4 \times 10^2$	$1 \cdot 4 \times 10^2$
Cs-137			$3 \cdot 2 \times 10^2$	$3 \cdot 2 \times 10^2$
Ce-144			$4 \cdot 5 \times 10^{-1}$	$4 \cdot 5 \times 10^{-1}$
Pu-238	$0 \cdot 0$	$0 \cdot 0$	$0 \cdot 0$	$0 \cdot 0$
Pu-239	$2 \cdot 7$	54	$3 \cdot 8 \times 10^{-3}$	$3 \cdot 8 \times 10^{-3}$
Pu-241	$7 \cdot 8 \times 10^{-2}$	$1 \cdot 56$	$2 \cdot 5 \times 10^{-2}$	$2 \cdot 5 \times 10^{-2}$
Am-241	$9 \cdot 1 \times 10^{-1}$	$18 \cdot 2$	$1 \cdot 5 \times 10^{-2}$	$1 \cdot 5 \times 10^{-2}$
I-131			$5 \cdot 6 \times 10^{-1}$	$5 \cdot 6 \times 10^{-1}$
I-129			$5 \cdot 0 \times 10^{-3}$	$5 \cdot 0 \times 10^{-3}$
S- 35			$1 \cdot 2$	$1 \cdot 2$
External			$1 \cdot 7 \times 10^3$	$1 \cdot 7 \times 10^3$
Total	$3 \cdot 7$ (0·1% of total)	$73 \cdot 76$ (3% of total)	$2 \cdot 6 \times 10^3$ (99·9% of total)	$2 \cdot 6 \times 10^3$ (97% of total)

Total dose from Sellafield discharges $= 2 \cdot 7$ mSv

*Quality factor for high LET radiation $= 20$

Quality factor for low LET radiation $= 1$

[+] See Table 4.11 for key to abbreviations for radionuclides (page 83)

(From NRPB R171, 1984; Table 8.1c)

Table 4.6 Radiation dose to red bone marrow from Windscale fire from 1950–1970 for an individual in a cohort of those born in Seascale in 1950 and resident in Seascale until 1970.

Radionuclide[+]	High LET dose (μGy)	High LET dose equivalent (μSv*)	Low LET dose (μGy)	Low LET dose equivalent (μSv*)
Ru-106			2·4	2·4
Cs-137			$1·2 \times 10^2$	$1·2 \times 10^2$
Ce-144			$1·6 \times 10^1$	$1·6 \times 10^1$
Pu-239	3·9	78	$5·4 \times 10^{-3}$	$5·4 \times 10^{-3}$
I-131			7·5	7·5
Po-210	10	200	$1·0 \times 10^{-5}$	$1·0 \times 10^{-5}$
Tc-132			$4·0 \times 10^1$	$4·0 \times 10^1$
External			$3·7 \times 10^2$	$3·7 \times 10^2$
Total	13·9 (2·4% of total)	278 (33% of total)	$5·6 \times 10^2$ (97·6% of total)	$5·6 \times 10^2$ (67% of total)

Total dose to red bone marrow = 0·838 mSv

*Quality factor for high LET radiation = 20
 Quality factor for low LET radiation = 1
[+] See Table 4.11 for key to abbreviations for radionuclides (page 83)

(From NRPB R171, 1984; Table 8.2c)

4.47 It is generally assumed that the relationship between dose received and number of leukaemias or cancers induced is linear. However there is considerable evidence both from radiotherapy experience with patients and from animal and *in vitro* work that this assumption probably produces an over-estimate of the number of cases induced by radiation at low dose rates when low LET radiation is being considered, because repair of damaged DNA can occur to a greater extent at low dose rates. Nevertheless, if we assume a linear relationship, thus making a further 'worst-case' assumption, then the dose received by the 1950 cohort from the Sellafield discharges can be calculated to be expected to give rise to a maximum of 13% of 0·1 additional cases of leukaemia (see paragraph 4.45) or 0·013 cases. If one considers the entire Seascale population under 20 up to 1980 then the expected number of additional cases can be similarly calculated to be about 0·013 × 7 = 0·091 cases. (There are some simplifications in this calculation since the cohorts born after 1960 have not had 20 years exposure and therefore have a reduced risk of leukaemia. In addition the doses calculated as being received by the different cohorts varies (see Figure 4.2)).

4.48 Table 2.1 (page 13) lists 4 deaths under age 20 from leukaemia in Seascale since 1955 (cases 1, 3, 5 and 6). NRPB calculate that 0·5 deaths from leukaemia would be expected during this period (paragraph 4.45). If 3·5 mSv average exposure per person up to the age of 20 years is expected to give rise to 0·091 additional leukaemia deaths in a population of about 1,200 children, then for irradiation to cause the additional 3·5 deaths found in Seascale in the same number of children, 135 mSv or 39 times the calculated dose equivalent would have to have been received by every person 20 years old or less during their 20 years or less residence in Seascale since 1945 from all the discharges and accidents at Sellafield since the plant opened in 1952. *In summary, background radiation would be expected to cause 0·5 deaths from leukaemia; additional radiation exposure from the discharges would be expected to cause less than 0·1 deaths from leukaemia; in fact 4 deaths from leukaemia in under 20 year-olds were observed in Seascale during the period under consideration.*

Figure 4.2 Percentage contribution to risk of radiation-induced leukaemia to age 20 or 1980 (whichever is earlier) for each cohort

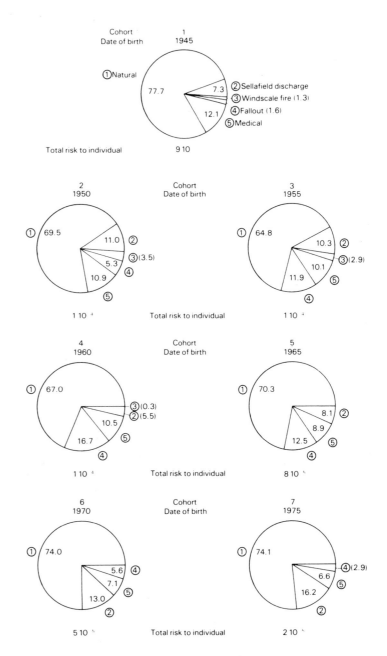

4.49 By calculating the expected number of cases of leukaemia from the maximum number that can be induced by natural background we avoid having to make any assumptions about risk factors for leukaemia mortality using high dose rate radiation since we are able to use background radiation as our standard and this is itself low dose-rate radiation.

4.50 It is very unlikely that the risk of dying from leukaemia due to the discharges is as high as has been calculated in paragraph 4.48 above. The largest risk factor for death from leukaemia used by UNSCEAR is about one half of the risk factor used above (see Table 4.4) and is only recommended for *in utero* exposure of the foetus; lower risk factors being recommended after birth. All the available evidence suggests that low dose rate low LET radiation is probably less effective than higher dose rate low LET radiation (paragraph 4.47). Finally, the assumption that the number of deaths expected in the 1950 cohort can simply be multiplied by 7 to give the number

71

of cases expected in the entire exposed population from 1945–1975 probably over-estimates the number of cases by a factor of 2. Taking all these factors into account there could be an additional safety factor of 10 involved and the actual additional dose required to produce the additional deaths from leukaemias at Seascale could in fact approach nearer to 400 times that calculated as being received by the young people.

4.51 We do need to consider carefully the assumptions made in arriving at our risk estimate to ensure that these assumptions do not significantly affect the calculation above (paragraphs 4.46–4.50). We shall do this in the following paragraphs.

4.52 High LET radiation is more biologically effective at low doses as compared with low LET radiation, probably because the cell is less able to repair high LET radiation (see Annex to this Chapter) and there are more uncertainties about its biological effects. Therefore if the contribution from high LET radiation were greater in the discharges than in background radiation this could be a source of error. In fact, background sources contribute 4% of the total biologically effective dose as high LET radiation (Table 4.3), an identical proportion to that contributed by the Sellafield discharges (Table 4.5). The high LET component from the Windscale fire is greater at 33% of the total (Table 4.6) and introduces a small amount of uncertainty, but the Windscale fire contributes less than 20% of the total dose from discharges to people in the 1950 cohort. This difference is unlikely to result in significant differences in the number of expected deaths calculated above.

Possible routes of exposure to the radioactive discharges

4.53 The routes of intake thought to give rise to the greatest dose to the population as a whole are:

Shore sand —inhalation of suspended radionuclides in sand;
Seaspray —inhalation of radionuclides associated with seaspray;
Fish —ingestion of radionuclides;
Crustaceans —ingestion of radionuclides;
Molluscs —ingestion of radionuclides.

Less important routes from the routine discharges to sea, which apply to a few individuals with unusual habits only, or which lead to relatively small intakes for the population as a whole are:

Seawater —inhalation of radionuclides during swimming;
—inadvertent ingestion of radionuclides in water during swimming;
Shore, silt and sand —inhalation of enhanced concentrations of radionuclides in air due to localised disturbances;
—deliberate ingestion of silt or sand and associated radionuclides;
Seaweed —ingestion of seaweed;
—inadvertent ingestion or inhalation of material associated with seaweed;
Beach debris —inadvertent ingestion or inhalation of material associated with beach debris.

Details of the assumptions and estimates made by NRPB in calculating the doses to red bone marrow are contained in the NRPB report, Chapter 4 and Chapter 9 (NRPB R171, 1984).

Atmospheric discharges

4.54 Atmospheric discharges are small in comparison to aqueous discharges (Figures 3.5–3.11, pages 47–53). Atmospheric discharges are dispersed and diluted in air as they travel downwind from the point of release, they are subsequently transferred through terrestrial food chains and inland water bodies such as reservoirs and rivers. Their contribution to marine levels of radioactivity is insignificant. Some monitoring of terrestrial food chains is carried out but this is not believed to be a significant pathway of exposure. For their dose estimations NRPB relied largely on models plus extrapolation from levels in milk which is subject to more intensive monitoring.

External doses

4.55 Radionuclides deposited on the ground and on the beaches will result in whole body absorbed doses from penetrating gamma radiation only. Beta and alpha rays are not sufficiently penetrating to contribute to this dose. Gamma ray doses have been measured at a number of locations in Cumbria by Cawse (NRPB R171, 1984), and the contribution of the Sellafield discharges to external doses from ground deposits is within geographical fluctuation of the natural gamma background radiation.

4.56 For their report NRPB did a more detailed gamma radiation survey of the beach at Seascale (Figure 4.3), which revealed that variation in levels across the beach is generally small and that the mean absorbed dose rate in air is 96 nGy/hr. Measurements were also undertaken at Drigg, and NRPB concluded that the gamma radiation dose at either beach does not vary significantly with location or activity on the beach.

Figure 4.3 Absorbed dose rate in air 1m above the beach at Seascale, April 1984

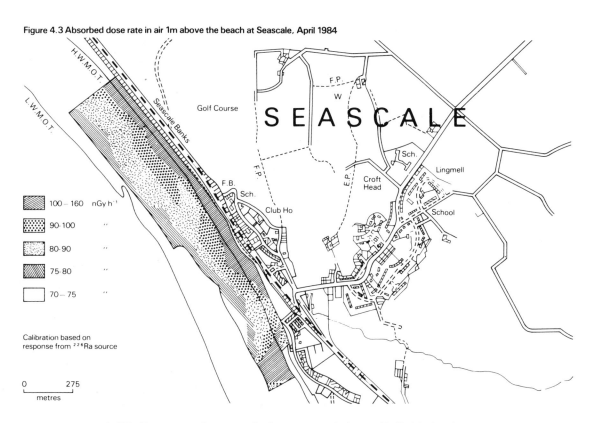

4.57 Doses to the population around the Sellafield site from the discharges of radiation into the sea and air are calculated from monitoring data on levels of the different radionuclides in the marine and terrestrial environments, carried out by BNFL, MAFF and the Department of the Environment. From this monitoring data predictions are made about the likely exposure of the population, based on a study of environmental pathways and on data from MAFF on local habits. The environmental monitoring programme has been modified over the years due to changes in the composition and magnitude of liquid and atmospheric discharges and also due to changes in the habits of the population, making certain pathways more or less important as routes for population exposure. Since the 1970s other agencies have also monitored different aspects of the environment in West Cumbria (eg NRPB, UKAEA, Institute of Terrestrial Ecology). There is now available a considerable body of data on the exposure of the population around Sellafield resulting from on-site operations. It must also be pointed out, however, that although all monitoring information was made available to the Group from as far back as the start of operations in 1952, the quantity and quality of the monitoring data from the earlier years are necessarily less good than the more recent results. MAFF habit surveys for fish and shellfish consumption have included a particular consideration of children in the last few years. There are few measurements on crustacea before 1970 and detailed measurements on crustacea and molluscs, including actinide levels have only been carried out since 1977. The NRPB report details all these points, and considers how much uncertainty these unknown factors in earlier years introduce into the dose estimates (NRPB R171, 1984; Chapter 4).

4.58 NRPB in their report consider that their estimates of concentrations of radionuclides in marine foods are probably accurate to within a factor of about 5 in most cases, although they state that for some less important radionuclides in some foods the uncertainty may be as great as a factor of 10 (NRPB R171, 1984; Chapter 4).

Habit surveys and critical groups

4.59 MAFF conduct habit surveys to establish local food consumption patterns and routes of external exposure. Based on these surveys 'critical groups' are identified. These are small groups of people with an unusually high consumption of particular foods, or with lifestyles that involve unusually prolonged occupancy of the shoreline area. The doses received by these 'critical groups' is calculated to fall within the ICRP recommended limit of exposure for members of the public per annum (5 mSv). It should be emphasised that these 'critical groups' can consist of relatively few people. These members of 'critical groups' are important in enabling an assessment of the maximum dose received by any member of the population in the area to be made, but are not so relevant to any risk estimate since the majority of the population under consideration will receive doses considerably below those received by the 'critical groups' (generally below 10–20% of the 'critical group' dose). It is these average doses to the population that are most relevent to any risk estimate, and these average doses were used in the NRPB report in calculating doses to red bone marrow. NRPB consider the effects of the doses received by 'critical groups' in more detail in Chapter 9.3 of their review (NRPB R171, 1984). The only extreme behaviour that has a significant effect on doses received is excessive sea food consumption. NRPB calculate that a 10 year-old child in the 'critical group' for sea food consumption will receive a red bone marrow dose equivalent greater than the average dose equivalent by a factor of 30. However it should be stressed that the number of children receiving such an increased dose will be a very small proportion of the total child population, and would not significantly affect the risk estimate calculations above.

Transfer factors

4.60 Monitoring activities plus habit surveys result in estimates of consumption of radionuclides in food. These are converted into estimates of doses to the tissues, using metabolic and dosimetric models, mainly derived from animal studies.

4.61 At the present time the main internationally recognised source of information on metabolic and dosimetric models for use in estimating radiation doses resulting from the intake of radionuclides are the recommendations contained in ICRP Publication 30, 'Limits for Intakes of Radionuclides by Workers'. The dosimetric models and metabolic data given in ICRP Publication 30 are intended for calculating Annual Limits of Intake (ALIs) for occupationally exposed adult workers, and are based on the behaviour in the body of chemical forms likely to be encountered in the workplace (mostly inorganic forms). There are difficulties in using these models for estimating doses to members of the public because of age-related variations in metabolic behaviour, organ size and separation and physiological parameters, as well as because of possible differences in the metabolic handling of radionuclides found in the environment compared to those in the workplace.

4.62 The NRPB have developed a methodology for the evaluation of doses to members of the public which takes account of changes in dose per unit intake with age as a result of growth of the body and body organs and for their separation, but metabolic behaviour is usually assumed to be the same as for the adult.

4.63 Some consideration has also been given to differences in metabolic transfer rates due to the physico-chemical forms of radionuclides which may be present in the environment, and revised values have recently been recommended for the gut transfer factor for the ingestion of organic forms of Plutonium associated with foodstuffs (0·05% transfer factor as opposed to the previously recommended 0·01% transfer factor). Further uncertainties are introduced here when young people are being considered. The gut wall is known to be more permeable to large molecules during the first few months of life prior to weaning, when maternal antibodies are absorbed from ingested milk. Animal feeding studies have confirmed that the neo-natal transfer factor for Plutonium species is around 100 times greater than that for adults, although it declines to adult values quite soon after weaning. There are no human data on such transfer factors in neo-nates. The enhanced values, which might be valid for infants on a milk diet in the first few weeks of life were not used to calculate doses to children as they are weaned onto a solid food diet after a few months (NRPB R171, 1984; paragraph 6.4.2). The use of slightly higher values is considered by NRPB in paragraph 10.2 of their review.

4.64 Table 4.7 summarises the gut transfer factors used in the above calculations of red bone marrow dose by NRPB. From Table 4.5 the major internal

Table 4.7 Summary of estimates of gastro-intestinal absorption applicable to the ingestion of radionuclides by children

Element	% absorption		
	First Year[1]	From 1 year[2]	ICRP value
Plutonium	0·5	0·05 (0·01– 0·1)	0·01
Americium	0·5	0·05 (0·01– 0·1)	0·05
Cerium	5	0·03 (0·01– 0·1)	0·03
Zirconium	5	1 (0·1 –10)	0·2
Ruthenium	10	5 (1 –15)	5
Polonium	20	10 (5 –20)	10
Lead	40	20 (5 –60)	20
Radium	40	20 (10 –30)	20
Strontium	60	30 (10 –60)	30
Caesium	100	100	100
Sulphur	100	100	80
Iodine	100	100	100

Values given are best estimates of absorption with possible ranges in parentheses.

[1] Used by NRPB in assessment of changed parameters in dose assessment (NRPB R171, 1984; Chapter 10).

[2] Used in main NRPB assessment (NRPB R171, 1984; Chapter 8).

(From NRPB R171, 1984)

contribution to the red bone marrow dose comes from Strontium-90, Ruthenium-106, Caesium-134 and Caesium-137. Caesium is assumed to have 100% gut transfer factor; Strontium-90 is assumed to have a 60% gut transfer factor in the first year and a 30% gut transfer factor in subsequent years, while Ruthenium is assumed to have a gut transfer factor of 10% in the first year and 5% in subsequent years. If these last two and all other low LET emitters consumed are assumed to have 100% gut transfer factors then the average low LET dose equivalent contribution from Sellafield emissions is increased to about 7·6 mSv, ie approximately treble the estimated dose equivalent, if all of the intake is assumed to be by ingestion; (in fact, some is by inhalation, for which a 100% transfer factor will already have been assumed). For high LET radiation, if the gut transfer factors were 100 times greater than the estimates used by NRPB, then the high LET contribution to the red bone marrow dose would be 7·4 mSv and the total dose to the red bone marrow would be increased four-fold (to 10·1 mSv).

4.65 Metabolic factors for children are not well known but are unlikely to alter doses by more than a factor of one or two and may well reduce the dose below calculated values since the biological half-life of many compounds is shorter in children than in adults.

Human Monitoring

4.66 The best way to confirm dose estimates is by monitoring children and adults for radionuclides. While it is possible to detect Caesium-137, Caesium-134 and Ruthenium-106 fairly readily by whole body monitoring, it is much more difficult to detect the alpha emitters, Plutonium and Americium in this way, and we were unable to obtain any data on alpha emitter levels in children.

Whole body monitoring

4.67 The whole body monitor on-site at BNFL is used to measure occupational exposure of workers and also provides a free service for any members of the public requesting monitoring. Many of those monitored by BNFL had low levels of Caesium-137, most had levels below 20 nCi (4,000 nCi maintained in the body would give an annual dose equivalent to the ICRP recommended limit). Some of this Caesium-137 dose could be contributed by nuclear fallout as well as by the discharges from BNFL. Since the gut transfer factor for Caesium-137 is 100% this information does not contribute information on the accuracy of any gut transfer factors. The results are however compatible with predictions on Caesium-137 levels expected from whitefish consumption.

4.68 In the voluntary monitoring carried out by BNFL only one of the approximately 200 people monitored was under 16. Following discussions with NRPB, they monitored volunteers from the Seascale population with a portable whole body monitor, to get some measurement of doses received by children in Seascale from all sources. They monitored more than 100 young people. From Table 4.8 it can be seen that only 2 of 112 young persons under 26 had detectable levels of Caesium-137 in their body, and that these 2 had levels below 15 nCi (0·6 kBq). These were below the levels calculated from environmental monitoring and habit surveys as likely to occur. NRPB will shortly be publishing the results of this study in greater detail (NRPB R172, 1984).

Table 4.8   Results of whole body measurements of body content of Caesium-137 for different age ranges.

Age in years	No of persons	Caesium-137 content			
		Not detected	0·6 kBq (15 nCi)	0·6–1·5 kBq (16–40 nCi)	1·5–3·7 kBq (41–100 nCi)
0– 2	5	5	0	0	0
3– 7	22	22	0	0	0
8–14	41	40	1	0	0
15–25	44	43	1	0	0
26 and over	178	159	15	3	1

(NRPB R172, 1984)

4.69 Post mortem assessments of tissue levels would be a possible source of information on human exposure. The limited data made available to us by NRPB, did not suggest that levels of Plutonium in members of the public in Cumbria were significantly different from levels in members of the public in the rest of the UK, but the data available were very limited.

4.70 In conclusion, although there were deficiencies in the monitoring programme, especially in early years, and in spite of some uncertainties about gut transfer factors for actinides and Ruthenium and the absence of human monitoring data for actinides, it seems likely that any deviation from normal plant operation that had health consequences would be detected by MAFF's monitoring activities, and that the doses to the red bone marrow calculated by NRPB in their review are based on reasonable 'best-estimate' assumptions.

Accidental Releases

4.71 The data above includes any discharges and emissions due to accidents occurring on-site at BNFL and resulting in off-site consequences. BNFL provided the Group with details of 14 incidents (including the November 1983 incident) that had occurred at Sellafield and which had involved abnormal releases of radioactivity into the environment between 1952 and December 1983 (BNFL, 1983). Apart from the Windscale fire (see below) none of these accidents are believed to have resulted in significant exposure to the public.

The Windscale Fire

4.72 The accident at the Windscale No 1 pile in October 1957 resulted in significant quantities of radioactive material being released into the atmosphere. During and after the fire various environmental measurements were made, including some measurements at Seascale. Levels of the main radionuclides in air at Seascale can be estimated from these data. Restrictions on the distribution of milk were imposed and reduced the potential population exposure as a consequence of the fire significantly. The milk from Seascale comes from a large area, but not generally from those farms closest to the Sellafield site (NRPB R171, 1984). In their calculations NRPB assumed 40% of milk consumed in Seascale was locally produced. Doses to individuals in the 1950 cohort from the Windscale fire are listed in Table 4.6. The high LET component of the dose from the fire is about 33% of the total dose equivalent.

The November 1983 Incident

4.73 In November 1983 there was an unplanned release of radionuclides (mainly Ruthenium-106) plus solvent and 'interfacial crud' (precipitated material between the organic and aqueous layers of liquid waste from the Sellafield site), which resulted in the beach between St Bees and Eskmeals being contaminated with unusual quantities of Ruthenium-106. In addition there was a small and transient elevation in Ruthenium-106 levels in mussels (MAFF Report, 1983) as a result of this release.

4.74 The consequences with regard to exposure of the public from this incident are believed to be small, and to relate mainly to the risk of a skin dose from skin contact with abnormally contaminated debris picked up from the beach and held over a significant period of time. It was this concern that led to the advice to the public not to frequent the beaches unnecessarily, which has now been revised. In the context of our investigation this hazard is not relevant since it is not believed to have resulted in a significant bone marrow dose likely to affect leukaemia incidence rates. There was evidence that a number of people on the beach at the time of the unplanned release may have ingested small amounts of Ruthenium-106; however the doses detected by whole body monitoring were at the limit of sensitivity of the machine.

4.75 There remain questions of concern with regard to this incident, especially whether similar occurrences could have taken place in the past and gone undetected. We questioned all relevant government departments and BNFL closely on this, and they told us that it was probable that such an incident would have been detected in the past. However, the incident did serve to underline several deficiencies in the on-site operation of BNFL most of which we believe have now been rectified. It also demonstrated that there can be even quite a large release of radioactivity from the site with small effects on the doses received by the adjacent population. The more intensive monitoring of the beaches precipitated by this incident did provide additional information on population exposure from the beaches. NRPB consider this route in their report.

Bone Marrow Model

4.76 Another possible source of error is the model used to calculate the dose to the red bone marrow. The assumptions behind the model are discusssed in NRPB R171, 1984; Appendix B. The model is not entirely satisfactory, in that it is one recommended for adults. There are problems with red bone marrow dose estimations for the alpha emitters because bone growth will distance the surface-seeking radionuclide from the active marrow and so reduce the red bone marrow dose.

SUMMARY OF RADIATION EXPOSURE OF THE YOUNG PEOPLE RESIDENT IN SEASCALE

4.77 Figure 4.4 from the NRPB review (NRPB R171, 1984; Figure 8.1) shows the annual absorbed radiation dose to the red bone marrow for the 1950 cohort discussed in paragraphs 4.21–4.52 up to 1980. Using their three risk estimates for leukaemia induction at different times in childhood (Table 4.4), NRPB have calculated the percentage contribution to the risk of radiation-induced leukaemia up to the age 20 or up to 1980 (whichever is the earlier) for the 7 cohorts born between 1945–1975 (Figure 4.2). For the 1950 cohort, contribution from the Sellafield discharges to the total radiation risk is 11%, with a further 3·5% contributed by the Windscale fire.

4.78 It should be noted that the contribution to the absorbed dose to red bone marrow and hence to leukaemia risk from the Sellafield discharges has increased for more recent cohorts; 16·2% of the total risk in the 1975 cohort was due to Sellafield discharges. The levels of discharges have reduced markedly in recent years and are expected to reduce further and this means the average percentage contribution to the risk for these cohorts over the full 20 years will be correspondingly less.

Risks for other cancers

4.79 These are dealt with in detail in NRPB Report (NRPB R171, 1984). Table 4.9 summarises these risks for 5 other sites as well as for red bone marrow, combining the results for all 7 cohorts. The contribution from the

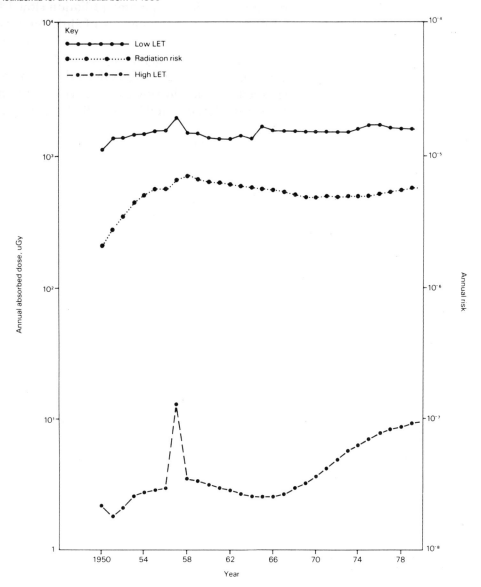

Figure 4.4 Annual absorbed dose to red bone marrow and risk of radiation-induced leukaemia for an individual born in 1950

Sellafield discharges and the Windscale fire combined is less than 15% of the total risk of radiation-induced cancer in all cases except that of the dose to the thyroid from the Windscale fire (53·9%) and the dose to the lower intestine from the discharges (24·3%).

Table 4.9 Predicted number of cases of radiation-induced leukaemia or other fatal cancers for all persons in Seascale up to age 20 or up to 1980 (for 1965 cohort and later cohorts) for all cohorts combined.

Tissue	Red bone marrow	Bone surfaces	Lung	Lower Large intestine	Liver	Thyroid
Predicted numbers of cases of radiation-induced leukaemia or fatal cancer from all sources[a]	1×10^{-1}	7×10^{-3}	1×10^{-1}	1×10^{-2}	1×10^{-2}	1×10^{-2}
% contribution from sources						
Sellafield discharge	9·1	10·1	1·1	24·3	8·0	13·8
Windscale fire	1·6	2·3	5·3	2·2	3·9	53·9
Fallout	9·2	10·5	0·9	12·5	5·8	4·8
Medical	10·1	6·9	0·9	7·6	8·8	1·7
Natural background	70·1	70·2	91·7	53·4	73·5	25·8

[a] Assuming 175 persons in each of 7 cohorts born from 1945 to 1975 at 5 year intervals.

4.80 The Group has considered the likely dose of (see Table 4.10) and possible effects from gamma radiation (low LET) and alpha radiation (high LET) to the red bone marrow of children in Seascale. The NRPB and other bodies at our request have provided much data and carried out measurements and preliminary analyses and evaluations. We have had access to existing unpublished data collected over many years by the various bodies charged with monitoring radioactivity in the environment. Three full reports from NRPB, requested by us, will shortly be published as NRPB documents.

Table 4.10 Summary of contribution of different sources of radiation up to 1970 to exposure for a Seascale resident born in 1950 in Seascale.

Source	High LET		Low LET	
	μGy	% of total high LET	μGy	% of total low LET
Natural Background	47	71	20×10^3	68
Fallout	1·7	3	$2·2 \times 10^3$	8
Medical Radiation	—	0	39×10^2	13
Sellafield Discharges	3·7	5	$2·6 \times 10^3$	9
Windscale Fire	13·9	21	$5·6 \times 10^2$	2
Total	66·3	100	29×10^3	100

High LET radiation forms 0·2% of the total dose from all sources of background radiation or 4·5% of the biologically effective dose using an RBE of 20.

4.81 The question we asked was *not* whether the absorbed doses of radiation from Sellafield discharges to Seascale children were and are within the recommendations of the relevant international committees. Rather we looked at the extent to which we believed it probable that radiation from the Sellafield site could be the cause of the increased incidence of leukaemia cases at Seascale. We therefore paid particular attention to comparing the doses received from background to those from the Sellafield discharges.

4.82 The dose from beta and gamma radiation from Sellafield discharges to Seascale children from ingested Caesium-137 in 1984 has been determined on a self-selected sample from direct measurement by NRPB. The results agree with those inferred from the MAFF studies of the pathways by which radioactive isotopes emitting gamma radiation are taken in by these children. The results show that it is very unlikely that any child currently receives more additional absorbed low LET radiation doses from ingestion than they already receive from the natural background. If any do, they will be exceptional, that is members of a 'critical group', and the doses they receive will still be comparable to those from background.

4.83 Background radiation in the UK varies from one area to another. So far as we know this variation is not reflected in the incidence of childhood leukaemia. The absorbed doses from gamma radiation that children receive from background will cause only a fraction of the normal incidence of childhood leukaemia. The investigations made of leukaemia after gamma radiation from accidental, military, or medical exposure have been analysed over many years to give estimates of risk which are used in recommending limits of radiation dose to radiation workers and to the public. The use of these factors with the measured and inferred gamma radiation absorbed dose from background gives an expected incidence of leukaemia of approximately one-fifth of normal. These factors are derived from high doses and if the risk factors for the low dose rates and low doses at Seascale are lower then the number of leukaemias caused by radiation would be less.

4.84 The situation for absorbed doses from alpha radiation is different from that for gamma radiation. Only about 0·2% of the absorbed dose from natural background radiation is alpha radiation or similar. However this proportion is similar to that estimated to have been received from the Sellafield discharges to sea by most Seascale children, although a few children who are major consumers of local shellfish may receive higher doses. Background radiation therefore provides a check on this situation also. However, the quantity of radioactive isotopes emitting alpha radiation in the children cannot be directly measured, but must be inferred from environmental and pathway studies. Such studies have been carried out for several years and more are being undertaken, but data on children and actinide exposure in the early years at the site is sparse and we shall never know for certain the levels of actinides in children in the area in earlier years.

4.85 Remote possibilities are that:

a. there is an unusual concentration of unusually susceptible children in the Seascale area;

b. there have been undetected discharges that have given rise to doses to the public greatly different to those believed to have occurred;

c. ingestion, inhalation and/or absorption of high LET emitters has been grossly under-estimated;

d. the model used to calculate red bone marrow doses is highly inaccurate.

4.86 Absorbed dose from alpha radiation in low doses at low dose rates has a much greater biological effect than the same dose of gamma radiation at low dose rate. The extent to which alpha radiation may cause more leukaemia in children than gamma radiation for the same dose cannot be found directly from any existing human evidence. Guidance can be obtained from other radiation-induced human cancers, from radiation-induced human adult leukaemia, and from the results of many animal experiments. This guidance is the basis of the recommendations on limits of radiation dose. Despite the uncertainties in these values we regard the relationship between the doses inferred for Seascale children and the doses from background radiation as an important check.

4.87 It has been assumed in our calculations that all deaths from leukaemia are due to the background radiation dose to the red bone marrow to provide 'worst-case' assumptions.

4.88 If all the assumptions are correct, these calculations have demonstrated that at most less than 0·1 deaths from leukaemia would be expected from the discharges (accidental and planned) from Sellafield to the under 20 year-old population of Seascale born between 1945–1975, giving a maximum risk of death from leukaemia of about 4 in a million young people per annum. This is approximately 1/40 of the additional number of deaths found at Seascale. To attribute these additional deaths from leukaemia to radiation it would require that the total discharges from Sellafield site had in fact been at least 40 times greater than reported and that monitoring and extrapolation of doses to the public were in error by a similar factor.

RECOMMENDATIONS   4.89 During consideration of the above data, we did find several areas where we felt that there could be improvements in the methods used to assess population exposure and in the controls placed by government upon industry. We therefore make the following recommendations:—

4.90 The chain of calculations leading to the assessed population dose is based on many assumptions and estimates. These are almost invariably maximising assumptions, however when a toxic agent is being considered, there is no substitute for direct measurement of that material in the exposed population.

4.91 Suprisingly there are few data on body levels of radionuclides in local people who are not workers at BNFL (at the start of our investigation only one measurement in a local child was available). The majority of those measurements that were available initially were made at the request of members of the public by BNFL (on a confidential basis) and not reported to authorising departments. We were told that the reason for the absence of human monitoring data on the general public was that human data were technically difficult to obtain, especially for the actinides. However, we were able to commission whole body monitoring of the residents in Seascale from NRPB once we pointed out the need for this information, and we felt the lack of data reflected, at least in part, a lack of appreciation of the value of such measurements. We recommend that more human monitoring data should be obtained, both locally in the area around the Sellafield site, and nationally and especially on children.

4.92 We were surprised at the lack of health input into this area, and the lack of co-ordination in the assessment of the overall impact of the discharges on the population. Each organisation we spoke to had considerable expertise in their particular area of environmental monitoring, but we were unable to identify any organisation that had the responsibility for assessing all of the information available and deciding on the overall implication of the discharges with regard to the health of the community. We recommend that there should be such a co-ordinating body, with a strong input by the DHSS and NRPB, that is able to ensure that more consideration is given to the adequacy of the data provided for dose assessment both in quality and quantity and to the need for research to improve the accuracy of dose assessment.

4.93 The authorisation of radioactive discharges appeared to us to be in too general terms; it had not been revised substantially since 1971 and did not include certain radionuclides discharged in considerable quantity. There was an incident in November 1983 which resulted in the beaches being contaminated to such an extent that the public were for a time advised not to use them unnecessarily. This was due to the release of solvent and quantities of radionuclides which fell within the authorisation; even if the public health consequences of the November incident were probably extremely small, the economic and social consequences to the community were much greater.

4.94 We therefore recommend that the Sellafield Authorisation should be revised and that tighter limits should be placed on the discharges of solvents and particulates, and that there should be limits on discharges over periods much shorter than three months.

References

Lord Adrian (1966): Radiological Hazards to patients; Final report of Committee. London, HMSO.

Beebe G Kato H and Rand C E (1978) Studies of the Mortality of A-bomb survivors: Mortality and radiation dose 1950–1974. Radiation Research 75 138.

BNFL (1983) Incidents at Sellafield involving abnormal releases of activity to the environment 1952–83 (SDB 239/W1).

Cawse P A (1980) Studies of environmental radioactivity in Cumbria, part 4: Caesium-137 and Plutonium in soils of Cumbria and the Isle of Man. Harwell, UKAEA, AERE—R9851.

ICRP Publication 30. Limits for Intakes of Radionuclides by Workers. Pergamon Press.

Monson R R and MacMahon B (1984) Pre-natal X-ray exposure and cancer in children in Radiation Carcinogenesis, Epidemiology and Biological Significance (Boice, J.D. et al eds). New York, Raven Press.

MAFF (1983) Incident leading to contamination of beaches near BNFL, Sellafield, November 1983, MAFF December, 1983.

NRPB R171 (1984) Stather J R Wrixon A D and Simmonds J R The risks of leukaemia and other cancers in Seascale from radiation exposure.

NRPB R172 (1984) Fry F A and Summerling T J Measurements of Caesium-137 in residents of Seascale and its Environs.

NRPB R170 (1984) Assessment of radiation exposure to members of the public in West Cumbria as a result of the discharges from BNFL, Sellafield. Linsley G S Dionian J Simmonds J R and Burges J.

Smith P G and Doll R (1982) Mortality among patients with ankylosing spondylitis after a single treatment course with X-rays. Br Med J 284 449.

Stewart A M and Kneale G W (1970a) Radiation dose effects in relation to obstetric X-rays and childhood cancers. Lancet, 1 1185.

Stewart A M and Kneale G W (1970b) Letter to Editor. Lancet, 2 1190.

Stewart A M and Kneale G W (1983) Letter submitted to Black Advisory Group, 15 December, 1983. (SDB 508/C3).

UNSCEAR (1972). Report of the United Nations Scientific Committee on the Effects of Atomic Radiation to the General Assembly.

UNSCEAR (1978). Report of the United Nations Scientific Committee on the Effects of Atomic Radiation to the General Assembly p 319.

Table 4.11   Abbreviations used for Radionuclides in Tables

Am	Americium
Cs	Caesium
C	Carbon
Ce	Cerium
I	Iodine
Pb	Lead
Nb	Niobium
Pu	Plutonium
Po	Polonium
Ra	Radium
Ru	Ruthenium
Sr	Strontium
S	Sulphur
Te	Tellurium
H-3	Tritium
Zr	Zirconium

ANNEX TO CHAPTER 4

RADIATION AND ITS BIOLOGICAL EFFECTS

A.4.1 Radiation is the transfer of energy through space or some other accommodating medium. One commonly experienced form of radiant energy is the heat from a fire, in which the energy from combustion of fuel is dissipated as warmth to those sitting in front of the fire without the temperature of the intervening air being significantly elevated. Ionising radiation is produced when one or more of the protons, neutrons and electrons, which make up the atoms of all elements, are released from an unstable mother element or radionuclide. We will not deal further with neutrons here since they are not relevant to the discharges from Sellafield. Electrons and protons are charged particles (electrons carry a negative charge, protons carry a positive charge), they are expelled from the mother atom at speed and travel through the atmosphere. Some of their kinetic energy is dissipated as they travel by the induction of charges on molecules in the medium they are travelling through. This is called 'ionisation'. Because these types of radiation are particulate they are not able to travel far before being stopped by collision with an atom of the medium they are passing through. Their energy may then be deposited in the material as a mixture of heat, ionisation and X-rays. When particles are emitted from such an unstable element or radionuclide, additional energy may be released in a non-particulate form, called gamma rays.

High and Low Linear Energy Transfer (LET) Radiation

A.4.2 Ionising radiation is recognised to be a carcinogen or cancer-causing agent, which acts by damaging the DNA in the chromosomes of the target cell. Damage due to low LET radiation may be repaired and more repair can occur when radiation is delivered at low dose rates than at high dose rates. This reduces cell killing due to low LET radiation at low dose rates. High LET radiation damage is less able to be repaired, and therefore for high LET radiation the biological effect per unit dose is relatively constant, irrespective of the dose rate.

A.4.3 Because X-rays and gamma rays were first used therapeutically and diagnostically the biological effect per unit dose for these low LET radiations was taken as the standard, and other ionising radiations are compared to X-rays. This means that the Relative Biological Effectiveness (RBE) of alpha rays and other high LET rays (as compared to gamma rays) increases as the dose rate decreases, and that at the very low dose rates relevant to background radiation, alpha rays may be between 20–50 times more biologically effective than gamma rays per unit dose. This is because X-rays and gamma rays become less biologically effective at low doses rather than because alpha rays become more biologically effective at low doses.

A.4.4 *Alpha rays (or particles):* These are helium atoms without their 2 outer electrons. They therefore carry a net positive charge and since they consist of 2 neutrons and 2 protons, have a mass of 4.

A.4.5 *Beta rays (or particles):* These are high energy electrons and are therefore negatively charged. They have a much smaller mass than alpha rays. If beta rays are stopped suddenly then their kinetic energy is converted to heat and electromagnetic radiation (X-rays).

A.4.6 *X-rays:* If a beam of high speed electrons (accelerated in magnetic fields produced from currents of hundreds of millions of volts), is suddenly arrested by interposing a dense material (eg tungsten) in its path, then some of the kinetic energy will be emitted as heat, but the rest will be emitted as short wave radiation of the same type as gamma rays, but with a continuous instead of discontinuous energy spectrum.

A.4.7 *Gamma rays:* These are a form of electromagnetic radiation, as are light and radio waves. The wavelength of gamma rays, however, is much shorter than that of light. Gamma rays can also be emitted by radionuclides in association with the release of particulate radiation.

A.4.8 Gamma rays and X-rays are the same form of radiation, but gamma rays are emitted by a radionuclide and have a single or discontinuous energy spectrum, whereas X-rays are produced by collisions of high speed electrons with other particles and produce a continuous energy spectrum (see A.4.6 above).

A.4.9 Radioactive decay in any given quantity of a radioactive element occurs at a constant rate, yet no one can tell at what time any particular atom will decay. What is certain is the period over which half of the material will have decayed, called the half-life ($T_{\frac{1}{2}}$). For example, if one starts with a gram of Radium-226, one will have half a gram of Radium in 1,600 years, a quarter of a gram of Radium in 3,200, ($2 \times 1,600$), years and an eighth of a gram of Radium in 4,800, ($3 \times 1,600$), years. The Radium will be decaying to its 'daughter products', ie other elements of lower atomic mass, many of which are also radioactive.

A.4.10 Each type of radiation emitted by radioactive materials interacts with other matter in important yet distinct ways. Alpha particles carry a charge of + 2 units. When an alpha particle passes near another atom, the electrons in its orbital shells are attracted to the alpha particle by virtue of their own negative charge. Some electrons are merely excited by the event, ie they move from a lower to a higher energy state while remaining in orbit round the nucleus. Many other atoms may lose their electrons entirely so that the atom is left ionised temporarily until it can recapture free electrons.

A.4.11 During this period of ionisation the atom may combine with other atoms in ways not usually possible giving rise to new, and possibly biologically active compounds. If the ionisation event takes place near the chromosomes in the cell, the reaction can result in the chromosomes being damaged, giving rise to mutations and impaired transfer of genetic information to daughter cells. These effects form the basis of the biologically adverse effects of ionising radiation. The ionisation of atoms in the path of the alpha particle results in the particle being slowed down in its path, and eventually the particle will stop.

A.4.12 Because of the density of the particle and its 2 positive charges, alpha particles have a very short range in biological material, of the order of a few micrometres. However they cause very dense ionisation over their path. They are called high linear energy transfer radiation particles (high LET particles).

A.4.13 Beta particles have far less mass and a single negative charge and therefore have a relatively low LET factor. Their biological effect is mediated via collisions with other electrons and nuclei to cause ionisation and greater chemical reactivity. As they are slowed down thay emit a small amount of X-rays.

A.4.14 Gamma (or X-) rays also have a low LET factor. They have no electric charge and no mass, however they can act like quantum particles in the same way as light does, and 'collide' with an electron, imparting kinetic energy to it and creating the equivalent of a beta particle. If no electron is encountered the gamma ray passes unchanged through the material. They are 'penetrating' radiation therefore and can pass completely through the body (as a proportion do when an X-ray film is made).

CHAPTER 5

RISK ASSESSMENT

5.1 In considering the assessment of risk, it is important to distinguish between *actual risk* during normal operation of the plant; *potential risk* should something go wrong; and *perceived risk*, which is not necessarily a true reflection of actual risk, and may be loosely equated with 'concern'. In Chapter 4 we have given some evidence that the *actual risk* of the Sellafield operation is comparatively low, provided that there are neither exceptional exposures, nor unusual susceptibility in particular individuals or groups, and that dose estimations are correct. The *potential risk*, given the scale of the Sellafield operation, must be greater. In this Chapter, we particularly examine the relationship between *actual* and *perceived risk*, which must be a factor in determining the degree of public concern.

5.2 In our daily lives we are all subjected to the risk of physical, microbiological, and chemical harm from the environment. Many such risks, although perceived originally as an inescapable part of life, have been substantially reduced, or even eliminated by modern science and technology. In the United Kingdom it would be reasonable to say that a substantial reduction in the risks from the environment affecting everyday life occurred during the past century, and that on average people are living longer because of these improvements.

5.3 As the number and severity of hazards in the environment has decreased, concern about the remaining risks, rather strangely, has increased.

5.4 Perhaps our perception of risks has been changed because any modern hazards (eg chemical and radioactive) are more difficult to understand and to assess than those of the past. Often they can be detected only by using complex equipment, and they produce chronic and delayed rather than acute and immediate effects. This has resulted in increasing public unease about these more subtle hazards in the environment, and if not properly controlled, the impact they may be having on people.

5.5 No one can completely eliminate all risk of harm, nor would it even be desirable for any person or government to try to do this in all cases. Few people would support a move to ban motor vehicles, yet 6,000 people are killed on the road each year (Central Statistical Office, 1984). Where the benefits are substantial and the risk to any single individual is comparatively small, the risk is generally accepted in practice, although where blame is proven damages and punishments may be imposed by society.

5.6 An important concept in controlling exposure to hazards is that of maintaining individual liberty. Since we do not all perceive the same risk as equally acceptable, it is normally conceded that any one individual may choose to expose himself to quite serious risks voluntarily, eg a mountaineer may accept the risk of death or serious injury while climbing, and it has been calculated that being President of the United States carries a 2% per annum risk of assassination, yet there continue to be candidates for election. There can be considerable opposition to the imposition of safeguards, as was the case with the introduction of legislation to ensure compulsory wearing of seat-belts.

5.7 When people are exposed to hazards without their knowledge or consent, and where there is little or no directly perceived benefit to those exposed to the risk, public expectations are greater, and people may talk of making things 'absolutely safe'. The development of cancer following unwitting and involuntary exposure to environmental carcinogens is a case in point. Apprehension is particularly strong where radioactivity is concerned, because of the military applications of atomic energy.

5.8 It is argued by some environmental groups that the nuclear energy industry should be closed down, and that we do not need nuclear power. Others point out that the present energy supply of the country depends on a certain proportion of the energy produced being derived from nuclear power stations which at present depend upon Sellafield for their continued functioning (Chapter 3).

5.9 We would suggest that the question to be considered is whether the discharges from the Sellafield site pose a greater hazard than other imposed, hidden, low exposures to long term hazards normally accepted by the public. In order to consider this question, it is necessary to find out what risks are generally found to be acceptable by members of the public.

5.10 The levels of fatal accidents averaged over broad areas of industry traditionally considered dangerous (quarries, mines, railways and the construction industry) are mainly between 1 and 3 in 10,000 annually, while in the manufacturing industry as a whole the level approaches 3 in 100,000. All these risks could be said to be freely entered into, although the additional incentive or benefit of financial reward has also to be considered (Royal Society, 1983). These risks are accepted by the occupationally exposed; the public will generally require a larger margin of safety.

5.11 A Working Party of the Royal Society estimated that most people are prepared to accept a risk of one chance in a million of dying in any one year from an environmental hazard, and would be reluctant to spend money or time on reducing such a risk further (Royal Society, 1983). As we considered in Chapter 3, this is of the same order as the average risk to populations from the discharges from Sellafield, even when they contain 'critical groups' (which represent small, highly exposed subgroups of the population) where exposure is below the ICRP recommended limit of 5 mSv per year.

5.12 From a decision on the accceptable level of risk, to a decision on the acceptable level of radionuclides in the environment, two extrapolations are necessary. First the radiation dose to people that would give rise to the acceptable level of risk must be determined, and then the level of radionuclides in the environment that will result in that dose being received by individuals in the population must be calculated. Monitoring can then take place to ensure that these levels in the environment are not exceeded.

5.13 In Chapters 3 and 4 we dealt with the problems of assessing population exposure from environmental measurements of radiation and in Chapter 4 we considered the evidence for deciding on the permitted doses to members of the public. There are problems with both of these extrapolations. There are areas of uncertainty surrounding the relative biological effectiveness of very densely ionising radiation such as that from Plutonium and Americium, when exposures occur continually at very low dose rates. There is no evidence from human exposures for the leukaemogenic dose to young people from chronic exposure to such radionuclides, all presently available evidence having been collected from acute exposures and most frequently from exposures to gamma rays.

5.14 The absence of human measurements in this area of risk assessment is not peculiar to the field of radiation protection, it is a problem encountered throughout the field of toxicology, where animal data is frequently all that is available for decision making. It adds a degree of uncertainty to the calculations.

5.15 In assessing the likelihood of potentially hazardous levels of radioactivity arising from the Sellafield operation, it is important to distinguish between the normal operation of the plant, and the effect of incidents such as that which took place last November. Since discharge of radioactive material is an intrinsic part of the operation, there must be some increase of radioactivity over the local background; similar local increases can occur in other ways, such as from the natural emissions from rocks and building materials, or the emissions generated in the combustion of fossil fuels (Corbett, 1983). Since the existence of any threshold for the carcinogenic effect of radiation is unproven, and may even be unprovable, the 'no risk' hypothesis is inadmissible; but extensive monitoring has indicated that the increased radioactivity in the general environment is of an order which is accepted in other situations. The occurrence of incidents introduces a new order of unpredictability, with the possibility of local hazards arising from abnormal discharges of radioactive material in concentrated form. Future effort on the normal operation of the plant, as is indeed already planned, should take the form of diminishing discharges still further, and aim to prevent further incidents.

5.16 The doses to the public living in the area around Sellafield are not in excess of the ICRP recommended limits (Chapter 4), and using the most conservative estimates, the risk to the under 20 year-old population with regard to death from leukaemia has been calculated to be of the order of 4 in a million, after making certain assumptions. As described in Chapter 4 this order of risk would be expected to give rise to less than 0·1 additional deaths from leukaemia before the age of 20 in the approximately 1,200 children born in Seascale between 1945 and 1975.

5.17 However, there is epidemiological evidence which indicates that the incidence of leukaemia is above this and above average both in the village of Seascale and in the rural district in which that village lies. It is in the nature of an average that a proportion of its components will fall above it; so it becomes a matter of judgement at what level a raised incidence of leukaemia becomes significant. To put the matter in general terms, the incidence of leukaemia in Seascale is unusual, but not unique; and we acknowledge that those who have drawn attention to it may have performed something of a public service. However, the suggestion that in the neighbourhood of Sellafield there is a causal relationship between an increased level of radioactivity and an above-average experience of leukaemia, while it is possible, is by no means proven. The causes of leukaemia are not fully established, even though radiation is one acknowledged factor; and the risk estimates calculated in Chapter 4 suggest that the doses received by the population are insufficient to account for the additional cases of leukaemia in the area. On the other hand, the proposition cannot be completely discounted, and it is difficult to see what scientific evidence would suffice to do so. The risk estimate we have calculated, if based on accurate assumptions about the dose received, is comparable to other risks to members of the public of everyday life normally accepted as reasonable by members of the public for human activities conveying some measure of benefit on society, such as other methods for the generation of energy or methods used for the production of food.

References

Central Statistical Office. Annual Abstract of Statistics, (1984) HMSO.

Corbett J O (1983). The Radiation Dose from Coal Burning; A Review of Pathways and Data. Radiation Protection Dosimetry *4* (i) 5–19 (SDB80/EV4).

Risk Assessment: Report of a Royal Society Study Group (1983) The Royal Society.

CHAPTER 6

CONCLUSIONS AND RECOMMENDATIONS

6.1 Our group was set up following a programme produced by YTV, and shown on the national network on Tuesday 1 November 1983. The programme alleged that there had been an excess of young people with leukaemia and other cancers in the neighbourhood of the Windscale plant for reprocessing nuclear fuel situated on BNFL's Sellafield site. The whole programme aroused considerable local and national concern.

6.2 The hypothesis in the television programme that the proximity of Sellafield to the village of Seascale could be a factor in producing cases of childhood leukaemia is not one which can be categorically dismissed, nor on the other hand is it easy to prove.

6.3 In the course of our inquiries we were made aware of what were considered by local doctors and others to be additional unusual concentrations of people with leukaemia, other tumours and Down's Syndrome. The mortality and cancer registry statistics which we examined in Chapter 2 included some material concerning older age groups and other cancers and did not support the suggestion that there was any unusual incidence of cancer in people aged over 24 or in other areas of West Cumbria. Down's Syndrome falls outside our terms of reference and for this reason we have not examined in detail the evidence relating to the incidence of Down's Syndrome in Maryport. We do, however, believe that this matter might be investigated further by detailed studies of maternal age-specific rates of the incidence of congenital disease in the population of the area.

6.4 The number of children who have developed leukaemia in a 30 year period in Seascale was less than 10. This is a relatively small number of cases. Because of uncertainty about the size of the population from which they are drawn the true incidence of leukaemia cannot be determined precisely. The fact that the final estimate of health risk has to be based on data which include those used to raise the hypothesis makes assessment of the significance of the observed incidence of leukaemia difficult. However, taking West Cumbria as a whole, mortality from childhood cancer is near to the national average, particularly for cancers other than leukaemia, but this does not exclude local pockets of high incidence.

6.5 In the Northern Children's Cancer Registry region, which contains 765 wards, Seascale had the third highest 'lymphoid malignancy' rate during 1968–82 in children under fifteen years of age in one study (this excess being entirely due to an increased incidence of leukaemia). Also, Millom Rural District (which includes Seascale) had the second highest rate among 152 comparable-sized Rural Districts in England and Wales, ranked according to mortality from leukaemia among people under the age of 25 during 1968–78. Mortality rates for other diseases in the local population, either of children or adults, are not unusual. In particular the overall mortality rate for young people under 25 in Millom Rural District is within normal limits (Chapter 2).

6.6 The Sellafield site contains a nuclear operation which is unique in the United Kingdom in terms of scale and complexity. The Windscale plant reprocesses not only the radioactive materials which are generated locally from the Calder Hall power station, but also materials brought from other nuclear power stations in the UK and imported from Italy and Japan (the imported material representing around 10% of the total material handled). The radioactive materials introduced into the plant contain a complex mixture of radioactive and non-radioactive chemicals. In order to reprocess this material and separate out the isotopes of value, large scale physico-chemical operations have to be undertaken. The unwanted radioactive materials (gaseous, liquid and solid) then have to be converted into a form suitable for either safe storage or planned disposal (Chapter 3).

6.7 While there is ample evidence of a real and sophisticated concern with the safe operation of the plant, which after all must be a major concern of those who work there, it has to be said that some of the plant was installed many years ago.

6.8 In any complex system there resides the possibility of human error. This was exemplified by the incident in November 1983 shortly after we started our inquiries. Even without such error, the possibility of accident remains, as in the 1957 fire. However, the risks to the public of the Sellafield operation should not be judged against the standard of 'total or absolute safety', which is quite unattainable in any human activity. A more realistic standard of comparison would be to the overall risks to the public from public transport or from deriving energy from coal or oil. The fact that no operation can be made absolutely safe does not conflict with the desirability, indeed the necessity, of making it as safe as is practicable.

6.9 Population exposure to radiation is at present inferred from environmental measurements of radionuclides in air, soil and food. This can only accurately reflect actual exposure if all possible routes from the environment to man are considered and if transfer factors used to calculate doses from environmental levels of radiation are known with certainty (Chapter 4).

6.10 It is impossible to establish for certain the situation with regard to environmental levels of radiation around Sellafield twenty or thirty years ago, and we shall never know the actual doses received by those children subsequently contracting leukaemia. In addition one cannot completely exclude the possibility of unplanned discharges which were not detected by the monitoring programmes and yet delivered a significant dose to humans via an unsuspected route.

6.11 Subject to the uncertainties described above, the NRPB provided us with a 'best estimate' of the average radiation dose to the red bone marrow received by a model population of the young people in Seascale. We then made a 'worst-case' assumption that leukaemia in under 20 year-olds in England and Wales is entirely due to the dose of background radiation received by the red bone marrow, and on this basis we estimated the risk from low dose rate radiation exposure. Using this risk estimate and a simple relationship between dose and effect, we were able to calculate the number of additional deaths from leukaemia in under 20 year-olds in Seascale that might be attributable to the additional dose their red bone marrow received from the discharges from the Sellafield site up to 1980. The number of deaths from leukaemia thus calculated is not sufficient to account for the deaths actually observed in Seascale, being around 20% of the number expected from background radiation (Chapter 4, paragraph 4.45).

6.12 These calculations do not support the view that the radiation released from Sellafield was responsible for the observed incidence of leukaemia in Seascale and its neighbourhood. However, it is important to stress the unavoidable uncertainties on dose in this situation, and the model we have used does not exclude other possibilities.

6.13 We have found no evidence of any general risk to health for children or adults living near Sellafield when compared to the rest of Cumbria, and we can give a qualified reassurance to the people who are concerned about a possible health hazard in the neighbourhood of Sellafield. However there are uncertainties concerning the operation of the plant, which were highlighted in the Nuclear Installations Inspectorate report of the November 1983 incident, and also problems attendant on the functioning of a plant, part of which has been long in service. There are further questions concerning the adequacy of the controls over present permitted levels for discharges; the quantitative assessment of apparent excesses of cancer; and possible genetic risks. During our investigations we also found some evidence of lack of co-ordination between the various agencies with an interest in this industry and considering its impact on the health of the community (Chapter 4).

RECOMMENDATIONS

6.14 In the interests of enhancing public safety, we believe that these matters should be addressed, and we therefore make the following recommendations. Our terms of reference relate mainly to epidemiological aspects of the problem, but we could not avoid the consideration of other matters during the investigation, in some of which we are unable to claim any special expertise.

I. Epidemiological (Chapter 2)

Recommendation 1

A study should be carried out on the records of those cases of leukaemia and lymphoma which have been diagnosed among young people up to the age of 25, resident in West Cumbria. These cases should be compared with suitable controls in respect of factors that could be relevant to the development of leukaemia and lymphoma.

Recommendation 2

A study should be carried out of the records on all children born since 1950 to mothers resident in Seascale at the time of birth. Its main purpose would be to examine cancer incidence and mortality among those children, including cases which might have occurred after moving from Seascale.

Recommendation 3

A study should be considered of the records of school children who have attended schools in the area.

Recommendation 4

The Northern Children's Cancer Registry should be asked to re-analyse their data using 1961, 1971 and 1981 population Census data where appropriate. Also stratification for age at diagnosis, and grouping by electoral ward at birth (as well as at diagnosis) should be undertaken, to determine the contribution these factors make to the incidence of leukaemia at Seascale.

Recommendation 5

We were impressed by the amount of data made available to us, and feel that encouragement should be given to an organisation such as OPCS or MRC to co-ordinate centrally the monitoring of small area statistics around major installations producing discharges that might present a carcinogenic or mutagenic hazard to the public. In this way early warning of any untoward health effect could be obtained.

II. Health Implications of Radioactive Discharges (Chapter 4)

Recommendation 6

More attention should be concentrated on measuring doses of radiation actually received by members of the public in West Cumbria and in other relevant areas, including control areas using whole body monitors, cytogenetic techniques and measurements of urinary and faecal radionuclides as appropriate and feasible. Much of such work is best carried out at a local level, but the ultimate responsibility for seeing that this type of monitoring is carried out should lie with the Health Departments so that it may be systematically and properly co-ordinated throughout the United Kingdom.

Recommendation 7

More work should be carried out on:

a. the gut transfer factors at present used, especially for children, with special attention being paid to radionuclides where this factor is believed to be low, and to organic forms of radionuclides;

b. the metabolic differences between adults and children with a view to improving the models used;

c. studies on children's habits in relation to the possibility that unknown critical pathways exist which are peculiar to children;

d. comparisons of the biological effects of low dose rate irradiation from alpha emitters with the biological effects from beta and gamma emitters both *in vitro* and *in vivo*.

Recommendation 8

Where discharge authorisations are considered particular attention should be paid to the upper limit placed on discharges over short periods of time; to the removal of solvent from discharges; the adequacy of filter systems to remove particulate material and to the limits imposed on specific radionuclides.

Recommendation 9

There should be a critical review of the necessity for discharges of alpha as well as beta/gamma emitters in discharges from BNFL Sellafield site to be significantly in excess of those from similar plant in other countries.

III. Regulatory Mechanisms (Chapter 4)

Recommendation 10

The controls imposed upon BNFL by government, and the ways in which these are reviewed should be revised so that:

a. reviews of the authorisations take place more frequently;

b. greater emphasis is placed on the collection and consideration of relevant epidemiological data and any other human data relevant to the possible health consequences of discharges;

c. there is formal consultation by the authorising department with Health Departments and NRPB on the possible health consequences of discharges;

d. the responsibility for monitoring and for interpretation of the results of monitoring this potentially serious environmental pollutant should be more clearly defined by government; these results of monitoring need to be considered in their entirety on a regular basis by a designated body *with significant health representation*, thus enabling decisions on action with regard to the control of permitted discharges to take account of all relevant factors.

LIST OF MEMBERS OF SIR DOUGLAS BLACK'S ADVISORY GROUP

CHAIRMAN

Sir Douglas Black MD FRCP
The Old Forge
Whitchurch on Thames
Oxfordshire

MEMBERS

Dr A M Adelstein MD FRCP FFCM
Epidemiology Department
London School of Hygiene and Tropical Medicine

Professor R J Berry MA DPhil MD FRCP FRCR
Department of Oncology
The Middlesex Hospital Medical School

Professor M Bobrow DSc MRCPath
Paediatric Research Unit
Guy's Hospital Medical School

Dr M J Gardner BSc PhD
MRC Environmental Epidemiology Unit
Southampton General Hospital

Professor J S Orr DSc FInstP FRSE
Department of Medical Physics
Royal Postgraduate Medical School

Professor G Rose MA DM DSc FRCP FFCM
Epidemiology Department
London School of Hygiene and Tropical Medicine

OBSERVERS

Dr A D McIntyre MB DPH DIH FFCM MRCPE
Scottish Home and Health Department

R A Page BSc CChem MRSC Barrister at Law
Welsh Office

SECRETARIAT

Dr Eileen D Rubery MB PhD DMRT FRCR (Medical)
Department of Health and Social Security

Lawrence Eaton MA (until 21 January 1984) (Administrative)
Department of Health and Social Security

Peter G Dibb (from 7 May 1984) (Administrative)
Department of Health and Social Security

ORGANISATIONS AND INDIVIDUALS WHO GAVE ORAL EVIDENCE TO THE GROUP OR TO THE SECRETARIAT

Organisation	Name	Title
British Nuclear Fuels plc	Mr C Allday	Chairman
	Mr R L Pilling	Director Reprocessing Operations
	Mr P W Mummery	Director Health and Safety
Institute of Cancer Research, Chester Beatty Research Institute	Dr R A Weiss	Director
Childhood Cancer Research Group, Oxford	Dr G J Draper	Director
Department of Community Medicine & General Practice, University of Oxford	Dr P Cook-Mozaffari	MRC External Staff
Department of the Environment	Dr A Duncan	Head of Radiochemical Inspectorate Branch
Greenpeace	Mr P Wilkinson	Director
Manchester Children's Tumour Registry	Dr J M Birch	Research Fellow in Oncology
Ministry of Agriculture, Fisheries & Food	Mr A Preston Dr N T Mitchell Dr G J Hunt Mr D F Jeffries	Directorate of Fisheries Research
National Radiological Protection Board	Mr H J Dunster	Director
	Dr R H Clarke	Secretary
	Dr J A Dennis	Assistant Director (Research and Development)
	Mr G A M Webb	Assistant Director (Operations)
	Dr J W Stather	Staff Member
	Dr A D Wrixon	Staff Member
	Dr J R Simmons	Staff Member
Northern Children's Tumour Registry	Dr A W Craft	Paediatrician
Nuclear Installation Inspectorate	Mr J A Driscoll	Superintending Inspector
	Mr L Clark	Principal Inspector
Office of Population Censuses & Surveys	Dr M Alderson	Chief Medical Statistician
Political Ecology Research Group	Mr P Taylor	Director
Yorkshire Television	Mr J Cutler	Producer, Documentaries
	Mr J Willis	Editor, Documentaries and Current Affairs
Individuals who gave oral evidence	Mr J Urquhart	Statistician
	Dr M K Palmer	Statistician

Organisation	Name	Title
HEALTH AUTHORITIES:		
West Cumbria	Dr J D Terrell	District Medical Officer
	Dr A Hargreaves	Community Physician
	Dr J Platt	Consultant Paediatrician
	Dr M B R Roberts	Consultant Paediatrician
	Dr T Bird	Consultant Haematologist
	Dr J M Kirk	Seascale General Practitioner
	Dr B Walker	Seascale General Practitioner
	Professor K Boddy	Head of Northern Regional Medical Physics Department
East Cumbria	Dr I H F Murray	District Medical Officer
	Dr P Tiplady	Specialist in Community Medicine
South Cumbria	Dr S D Horsley	District Medical Officer
	Dr E Jessop	Senior Registrar in Community Medicine

GLOSSARY

The terms below are to help the reader understand the text; they are not formal scientific definitions.

ACTINIDES
The group of fifteen elements with atomic numbers 89–103 which includes Uranium and Plutonium.

ADVANCED GAS COOLED REACTORS (AGR)
Nuclear reactors operating at high temperatures (over 1000°C), cooled by gas and utilising enriched Uranium oxide fuel.

ALARA (As Low As Reasonably Achievable)
The internationally accepted concept that the effects of radiation and levels of exposure of workers and members of the public should be kept as low as possible "with due regard to economic and social factors".

ALPHA EMITTER ($\propto$)
A radionuclide which emits alpha particles.

ALPHA PARTICLES/ALPHA RADIATION
A particle emitted during the radioactive decay of some radionuclides; it consists of two protons and two neutrons and has a net charge of $+2$. It is a high linear energy transfer radiation.

BECQUEREL (Bq)
The Standard International (SI) Unit for the number of radioactive disintegrations taking place per second in a material.
1Bq = 1 radioactive disintegration per second.
$1Bq = 27 \times 10^{-12}$ curies.

BETA EMITTER (β)
A radionuclide which emits beta particles.

BETA PARTICLES/BETA RADIATION
A particle emitted during the radioactive decay of some radionuclides. It has a mass and charge equal to that of an electron, (-1). It is a low linear energy transfer radiation.

CLADDING
The covering on nuclear fuel. Designed to resist physical and chemical effects thus preventing corrosion of the fuel and escape of products of the reaction.

COLLECTIVE DOSE COMMITMENT
Sum of the doses to all individuals in a population.

COMMITTED DOSE EQUIVALENT

The dose equivalent to the tissues resulting from a radionuclide that has been incorporated into the body will be spread out in time and will be delivered gradually as the radionuclide decays. The total dose equivalent to a tissue during the period of 50 years following the incorporation of a quantity of radionuclide into the body is known as the committed dose equivalent arising at the time of incorporation (measured in sieverts or rems).

COOLING PONDS

Areas of the Sellafield site where newly arrived fuel rods are stored under water to allow the decay of volatile, short half-life isotopes. The rods produce considerable heat which is removed by a flow of cooling-water through the ponds.

COSMIC RAYS

High energy extra-terrestrial ionising radiation. Mostly absorbed by the earth's atmosphere.

CURIE (Ci)

The old unit of radioactive disintegration. $1Ci = 3.7 \times 10^{10}$ disintegrations per second ($27Ci = 10^{12}Bq$).

DECANNING

The first process in the cycle of nuclear fuel reprocessing in which the casing (cladding) is separated from the fuel.

DECAY

The process by which radionuclides change from one atom to another emitting ionising radiation as they do so.

DISCHARGES

The release of liquid effluent from an industrial site.

DOSE EQUIVALENT

The quantity obtained by multiplying the absorbed dose by a modifying factor, the Quality Factor (QF) (measured in sieverts or rems).

EMISSION

The release of gaseous effluent from an industrial plant. Filters or scrubbers are employed to clean the effluent before its release to the atmosphere.

FAST BREEDER REACTOR

A type of nuclear power reactor which produces more fissionable material than it consumes.

GAMMA RAYS (γ)

Photons emitted from the nucleus of a radionuclide during radioactive decay.

GAS COOLED REACTOR (GCR)

A nuclear reactor which uses gas, usually carbon dioxide, to cool the pile. In Britain these reactors use "magnox" fuel.

GRAY (Gy)

The S.I. unit of absorbed dose.

1 gray = 1 joule of energy absorbed per kilogram of tissue.

1 gray = 100 rad.

HALF-LIFE ($T_{\frac{1}{2}}$)

The time for the activity of a radionuclide to decay to half its original value.

HEPA

High efficiency particle absorbers. A type of filter which removes particles from the gas passing through it.

ICRP

International Commission on Radiological Protection. Consists of experts in radiology, genetics, physics, medicine and radiological protection from a number of countries. Established in 1928, it meets regularly to consider the results of research on the effects of radiation, and publishes recommendations on acceptable dose limits for man.

IN VITRO

Studies carried out on material from an animal under artificially controlled conditions in the laboratory.

IN VIVO

Studies carried out in the intact animal.

ISOTOPES

Forms of an element having the same atomic number (number of protons) but different atomic mass (number of neutrons + protons).

LINEAR ENERGY TRANSFER (LET)

A measure of the density of energy deposition in the track of ionising radiation.

MAGNOX

A type of nuclear fuel which is encased in a Magnesium alloy. It is also the name given to the gas cooled reactors using the fuel.

OPCS

The Office of Population Censuses and Surveys. A British government body which collates and publishes data on disease, mortality and population effects in England and Wales.

OXIDE FUEL

Nuclear fuel consisting of pellets of Uranium oxide. Used in Advanced Gas Cooled Reactors and Water Cooled Reactors.

PILE

The name given to the part of a nuclear reactor which contains the fuel and their moderating systems.

PRESSURISED WATER REACTOR (PWR)

A type of nuclear power plant which has a pile cooled by water kept under pressure.

RADIONUCLIDE
A species of atom which is unstable and can undergo spontaneous transformation to another atom, during which it releases ionising radiation.

RADON DECAY PRODUCTS/RADON DAUGHTERS
Atoms produced from the radioactive decay of Radium. Many are radionuclides.

RAD
The old unit of absorbed radiation dose.
100 rad=1 gray.

RELATIVE BIOLOGICAL EFFECTIVENESS (RBE)
A factor by which the absorbed dose of radiation is multiplied to produce the effective dose. It allows compensation to be made for the differing biological effects of the various types of ionising radiation.

REM
The old unit of dose equivalent. The absorbed dose (rads) is multiplied by a quality factor representative of the relative biological effectiveness of the particular radiation.
100 rem=1 sievert.

REPROCESSING
A process, the purpose of which is to extract Uranium and Plutonium from spent fuel.

SELLAFIELD SITE
The composite name given to the BNFL site in W. Cumbria which includes among other things the Windscale nuclear fuel reprocessing facility and the Calder Hall nuclear reactors.

SIXEP
Site Ion Exchange Extraction Plant. New plant shortly to be commissioned at Sellafield which enables the levels of metals such as Caesium and Ruthenium in the liquid discharges to be reduced by absorbing them onto ion exchange resins.

SIEVERT (Sv)
The S.I. unit of dose equivalence. The absorbed dose (in grays) is multiplied by a quality factor representative of the relative biological effectiveness of the radiation.
1 sievert=100 rem.

STANDARDISED MORTALITY RATIOS (SMR)
The rate of death for a particular area after standardising for age, expressed as a percentage of the overall rate for England and Wales.

STANDARDISED REGISTRATION RATIOS (SRR)
The rate of cancer registration for a particular area, after standardisation for age, expressed as a percentage of the overall rate for England and Wales.

STAINLESS STEEL CLADDING

Cladding made of stainless steel which contains the fuel used in Advanced Gas Cooled Reactors (AGR) which operate at very high temperatures.

THORP

Thermal Oxide Reprocessing Plant. Plant shortly to be commissioned at Sellafield to permit reprocessing of enriched Uranium oxide fuel used by Advanced Gas Cooled reactors and Water Cooled Reactors.

WINDSCALE PLANT

The nuclear fuel reprocessing facility situated within the Sellafield site.

X-RAYS

Photons with an energy greater than 100 electron volts (eV) emitted from an atom as the result of change in its outer electron structure. Also produced by the rapid deceleration of free electrons.

ZIRCONIUM CLADDING

Cladding made of a Zirconium alloy which is used to protect the fuel in some Water Cooled Reactors.

Radiological units used in this report

Quantity	New S.I. Unit and Symbol	Definition	Old Unit and Symbol	Definition	Conversion data
Radioactivity	becquerel (Bq)	disintegration per second	curie(Ci)	$3 \cdot 7 \times 10^{10}$ disintegrations per second	1 Ci=$3 \cdot 7 \times 10^{10}$ Bq; 1 Bq=$2 \cdot 7 \times 10^{-11}$ Ci=27 pCi; 1 T Bq=10^{12} Bq=26 Ci
Absorbed dose	gray (Gy)	J kg^{-1} (joule per kilogram)	rad (rad)	10^{-2} J Kg^{-1}	1 rad=10^{-2} Gy; 1 Gy=10^{2} rad
Dose equivalent	sievert (Sv)	J Kg$^{-1} \times$(modifying factors)	rem (rem)	10^{-2} J Kg$^{-1} \times$(modifying factors)	1 rem=10^{-2} Sv=10 mSv; 1 Sv=10^{2} rem

Printed in the UK for HMSO Dd 737874 C20 7/84